Heal the Cause!

Creating Wellness - Body, Mind, & Spirit

By Valerie Seeman Moreton, N.D.

KALOS^{SM} TRANSFORMATIONAL HEALING
BOOK TWO

**KALOS PUBLISHING,
SAN DIEGO, CALIFORNIA**

HEAL THE CAUSE!

Creating Wellness - Body, Mind & Spirit

By Valerie Seeman Moreton, N. D.
Kalos^{SM} Transformational Healing, Book Two

Published by: **Kalos^{SM} Publishing**
P.O. BOX 270817
San Diego, CA. 92198-2817

 This book printed in the USA on recycled, archival-quality paper

Cover photo by Valerie Seeman Moreton, Photos by Joe Gibbs
Typesetting by Richard Cravy, Drawings by Zana Ziegler

Publisher's Cataloging in Publication
Moreton, Valerie Claire Seeman, 1938-
    Heal The Cause! : creating wellness--body, mind & spirit / by
Valerie Seeman Moreton.-- 1st ed.
    p. cm. -- (Kalos transformational healing; bk. 2)
    Includes glossary and index.
    ISBN: 1-882590-03-1: $19.50 Softcover

    1. LCCN: 96-75242   2. Naturopathy. 3. Mental/emotional Healing.
    4. Spiritual Healing.   I. Title. II. Series

RZ440.M67 1996   615.5'35
                                   QBI96-20100

Library of Congress Card Number 96-075242
                    See last page for ordering information

Dedication

This book is dedicated to my beloved husband, Douglas R. Moreton, who has given his valuable time and talents to the support of seeing that this entire series of books on Transfomational Healing is published. He has worked tirelessly in editing and contributing to the clarity, distinctions and quality of this work. He has been by my side, giving his all to serve God and humanity in his special way. For his support I am eternally grateful.

Acknowledgements *and* Appreciation

To Those Who Helped Get this Book to You

A special thank you to Max Skousen, whose devotion to God and commitment to create a process for lay people to participate in their healing and take charge of their lives, spearheaded and financed the initial project to "understand the cause." Max, who has written over 20 books, has devoted his life to supporting people to "Transform their lives by the renewing of their mind."

More thanks and appreciation to those who gave support and/or contributed to editing:

Peggy Allen (with her daughter Teri's support) and Jo Ellen Tropper took rough copy and insured its readability. They spent many hours, days and weeks to edit content and clarity. Deep appreciation goes to June Schnell (my mother-in-law) who contributed in numerous ways, including editing, to further this work. Dotti Nelson and Paul Gessford polished and clarified the content for readers of diverse backgrounds. Richard Cravy unselfishly gave countless hours for typesetting and technical support. Special acknowledgements go to Anice Longmore, Robyn Tanner and Joan Miller for giving me enthusiastic support and for their aspiration to have this work carried out to the world.

Special blessings and A BIG THANKS to all of them.

Table of Contents

A Guide Book to Healing the Cause and
Renewing Your Core Programming

SECTION I — *WHAT* IS THE CAUSE
AND *WHERE* DO I FIND IT?

Understanding the Cause — Natural Laws Govern the
Healing Process - Body, Mind and Spirit.

SECTION II — HOW DO I *UNCOVER* THE CAUSE?
Learning Techniques to *Uncover the Cause* through Muscle Response Testing (MRT).

SECTION III — HOW DO I *RESOLVE* THE CAUSE?
Integrating Principles with Techniques. A Step by Step Guide to *Heal the Cause* through the Kalos Process.

SECTION IV — BEING AT CAUSE?
Renewing the Mind through Universal Principles and Choosing to *Be at Cause*.

NOTE: Please read the Introduction first. When teaching this work, I like giving a principle first, then have students practice. For the ease of learning through this text I am covering the methodology in one section. My intention is to teach in a way that is easiest to learn - learn the principle, experience doing the technique, then put it all together while doing The Kalos Process.

All of the techniques are first taught in Section II and later integrated into The Kalos Process. You will benefit by practicing each technique as it comes up. Practicing the hands-on parts of this book as soon as possible will speed up your learning process.

DISCLAIMER

This book is sold with the understanding that the publisher and author are not engaged in rendering professional services or medical advice. This book does not take the place of the services of a competent health professional.

This book is not a treatment of any physical, mental or emotional illness. It is not a substitute for ongoing therapy (medical or psychological). It is not about giving advice on how to solve the problems of life. It is not about taking sides or establishing blame. It is not about deciding what is right or wrong. It is not a magic pill that guarantees the non-disturbed state. The laws and principles described in *Heal the Cause!* can assist you in creating profound differences in your life. It is your responsibility to make sure you utilize these concepts and methods with discretion.

Every effort has been made to make this text a complete and accurate introduction to the possibility of being healed. However, there may be mistakes both typographical and in content. Therefore, this text should be used only as a general guide and not as the ultimate source of information on transformational healing. Furthermore, this text contains information utilized by the author at the date of printing.

The purpose of this manual is to educate and inform. The author and Kalos Publishing shall have neither liability nor responsibility to any person or entity with respect to any loss or damage caused, or alleged to be caused, directly or indirectly by the information contained in this book.

If you do not wish to be bound by the above, you may return this book to the publisher for a full refund.

Introduction

After being in Wholistic General Practice for several years, I noticed that most people came back to be treated for the same or a similar problem. This aroused a strong desire in me to understand the source of their ailment, rather than continually working with their symptoms and surface causes. Even though I felt the apparent cause was being cared for through cleansing and nourishing their body, I felt in most cases there was a cause beyond the physical domain.

Based upon the belief that toxicity made the body sick, my question was: "Why was their body repeatedly becoming toxic?" I knew that people wouldn't keep getting the same problem again if the deeper cause was known and resolved. This brought me to exploring the mental, emotional and spiritual aspects of health as well, and to discovering the value of living from divine essence (spirit).

My experience taught me that living "in the now" versus "reactionary behavior" (from early childhood) gave me the skills to handle stressful situations maturely. If eighty percent of one's personality is set by the age of six, a need for mental rebirth or renewal is in order. Would that be possible, I questioned, as I ventured out to explore.

My research affirms that anytime we make a decision with great emotion attached, it becomes the subconscious "rule of action" from that time forth. This means that when an upset occurs, even at a very young age, like one or two, a decision is made (subconsciously) that influences the rest of your life. If that decision was that you were "not loved" or "not good enough," your whole life would be about compensating for that belief to prove it was false. Behaving in a particular way to get love or approval can cause self-defeating patterns to develop and defense mechanisms to form. And all of this is based upon a lie, founded upon fear instead of love.

Many *causes* are directly related to not knowing or not understanding how to live from spiritual consciousness rather than fear-based programming. This text includes methods to "see the reality" and commit to "telling the truth." You can gain understanding from your subconscious mind so that you are aware of what needs healing. Muscle Response Testing (MRT) is used as a tool to make discovery accessible to all.

Spiritual awareness is essential for renewing the mind. This means that one understands the reality by exposing the deception (like not being loved) and aligning with spiritual principles. Living in harmony with others requires accepting **who** you are. Acknowledging that you are a "being of love" opens the door to seeing others as the same. The problem is not an absence of love. The problem is *expressing* love in a mature way.

When your mind becomes your humble servant, the spirit and mind are no longer at odds with each other. You have an opportunity to be the master of your mind, instead of a victim of it. Through accessing subconscious programming and following the methods in this book, it is possible for you to be in control of your life in a vibrant way.

Your problem becomes easy to understand once you know how your mind works and learn how to access information from a subconscious level. My intention is to support people to understand and heal their problems at a causal level. On this premise I ventured out to learn and comprehend the physical, mental, emotional and spiritual aspects of health. I am sharing with you my findings so that you can begin to take more responsibility for your well-being and support others to do the same.

The foundation for The Kalos Process was developed over the past thirty years and the refining of the methodology for fourteen. I worked with a team of professionals who were interested in finding a way to teach lay people to transform their health and their lives. The vision was to assist people to play an active role in their healing by understanding their

2

problem at a *causal level* and *aligning themselves to the laws and principles of health.* Our intention was to develop and teach a simple method, which could be learned in a short amount of time. This methodology was designed to determine the actual source of the problem and empower people to take charge of their lives. By understanding and owning their core programming, usually based upon a self-deception, they could then choose to live out of the spiritual reality of their full potential and align themselves to the laws, precepts and principles of health.

The Kalos Process is not psychoanalysis, yet it links behavior to subconscious programming. Therefore, it does not require years of study and application to use. It is, however, a spiritually oriented process designed to expose the mistaken "core programming" behind a problem. Your awareness of what actually took place allows you to reprogram the past with honesty and clarity and to be set free from the deceptions that have resulted. Seeing what is "really so" transforms your attitude immediately and begins the healing process.

Our early childhood responses to others make up the largest part of our personality and behavior. You now have an opportunity to look at the old patterns which no longer serve you. They were created for survival by a small child trying to cope with an overwhelming world. They have worked well for survival. Now is the time to renew your mind to express your spiritual attributes and to live in your full potential.

You get to explore what is happening in the inner realms of the mind and emotions. You get to expose the hidden agenda that no longer serves you. Thoughts and feelings can become divided. You can <u>think</u> one way, yet <u>feel</u> quite differently. This condition causes conflicts which fog your mind and makes it difficult to achieve your goals, like going in two directions at once. We call this condition emotional dyslexia, as described in *Chapter Nine.* Major life issues can be resolved by exposing patterns underlying a person's behavior - *seeing* with "new eyes," and making new choices. During The Process, you'll discover WHY your early programming comes up every time a particular person or circumstance arises. Every time a decision is made with great emotion, (even love and hate can be attached to parents, siblings, etc.), it becomes the "rule of action" from that time forth. Have you ever wondered how "grownups" can act so immaturely at times? These life patterns are unveiled before your eyes, as you get to know your "little child" within.

Much of what you heal in The Process is done while looking through another's eyes. You can be present in their thoughts and feelings when the deception was created. Once you see "their truth" from this other perspective, you can then heal your own misjudgments and resolve your major issues.

It is amazing to see how many students return to say how their processing made a difference in other family members who were not physically present. Our supra-conscious mind seems to extend beyond the boundaries of our bodies, reaching out in some miraculous way, touching the lives of others. We are just beginning to tap the surface of the incredible dimensions of the human spirit.

The science behind the Kalos Process can be confirmed through your experiences in life. I encourage you to experiment with it and discover how easily you can achieve results. You can discover the power to transform your mind and consciously take charge of your life!

May you enjoy studying these laws of health, precepts of the mind and principles of the spirit. May you progress in understanding natural laws, learning The Kalos Process and surrendering to inner guidance. It is my hope that you heal yourself, then support the healing of others. Healing the underlying CAUSE can heal our world. God bless you!

— *Author*

"Spirituality is the highest acquisition of the soul, the divine in man. Spirituality, our true aim, is the consciousness of victory over self and of communion with the Infinite. Spirituality impels one to conquer difficulties and acquire more and more strength. To feel one's faculties unfolding and truth expanding the soul is one of life's sublimest experiences. Would that all might so live as to experience that ecstasy!"

David O. McKay

SECTION I

WHAT IS THE CAUSE AND WHERE DO I FIND IT?

Understanding the Cause
Natural Laws Govern the Healing Process — Body, Mind and Spirit

If you think something outside yourself is the cause of your problem, you will look outside yourself for the answer. Look within and BE HEALED!

Chapter One

Laws, Precepts and Principles

The Three Components of Transformational Healing

Transform your life to wellness by understanding the cause of any problem and aligning to the appropriate *law, precept*[1] or *principle* that was broken. **Every cause has its consequence.** Maybe all ailments are due to the breaking of natural laws.[2] Since we are all triune beings, any area of our functioning of body, mind, or spirit can be at cause. Like any great detective we look for clues in the following three realms of natural laws:

- PHYSICAL LAWS regulating one's body
- MENTAL PRECEPTS directing one's mind
- SPIRITUAL PRINCIPLES empowering one's life

---

[1]Precept, a direction given as a rule of action or conduct; a maxim; a procedural directive, as for the performance of, a technical process. (Webster)

[2]*Natural Law* (Glossary) is a principle or body of laws derived from nature, right reason, or religion and as ethically binding in human society.

9

You can promote healing in at least three different ways - aligning to *physical laws, mental precepts* and *spiritual principles*[3]. Each area has a valuable relationship with the other. You cannot separate the body from the precepts of the mind; for the mind controls the body. Likewise, you cannot separate the mind from spirit, as the principles ruling in the spiritual realm affect both the mind and the body. One domain of natural law is not better than the other, just different, inseparably connected and symbiotically functioning all the time.

You were created in such a marvelous way that healing comes naturally unless you have consciously or unconsciously interfered by breaking a natural law. The body always seeks balance. Natural laws take effect automatically to keep you well. I consider the techniques contained herein wholistic because of their multidimensional and multi-modality approach. I spell wholistic with a "w" because this way of spelling it includes the physical realm, whereas without the "w" (holistic), refers to "beyond the physical."

Understanding the Cause

Transformational Healing grants us the ability to understand WHY we got the problem in the first place. Unless we get to *The Cause*, the problem may return with similar symptoms or manifest itself in another way in an-

---

[3] See Glossary for distinctions in the definitions of: physical laws, mental precepts, and spiritual principles.

other area of the body. The cause can begin in any of the three realms, physical, mental, or spiritual, yet can affect any or all of those domains.

You can learn how to trace a problem to its cause and heal it. This is one of the biggest truly transformational breakthroughs in healing in the last 1,900 years. When the cause is understood and cared for, rapid healing takes place in the body. Problems become chronic because the cause is not corrected. Drugging and cutting the body usually does not take care of *The Cause*, they only alleviate the symptoms, hopefully. The Kalos methods uncover many problems by "seeing the truth," thus to be set free of the deception[4] creating or hiding the problem.

Each of these realms (body, mind, spirit) contributes to speeding up the process of complete healing. Each brings a benefit and supports the healing of the other domains. After you understand *The Cause*, you always want to support the physical body to repair and rejuvenate as quickly as possible. So, of course, you would use the proper nutrients and modalities of the physical level, even when the cause did not originate there. When the cause **does** originate in the physical realm, it is even more important to focus on and correct the physical law that has been broken. In book three, *The Manual*, you can learn how the same body that revealed the cause can also reveal which healing modality to use. The sequence, duration

---

[4]Deception (Glossary) - a perpetration, something you believe to be true, consciously or unconsciously, that isn't.

and intensity of support is all unveiled through the appropriate testing.

Your Beliefs Affect the Healing Process

When your mind says your body will now heal, it will. The mind controls the body. One of the first ways I support someone with a "terminal" problem is to test whether they want to live or die. You must want to live, consciously and subconsciously, in order to heal. Some people do not heal because they are double minded about it - part of them wants to, but another part doesn't. You will learn how to test this in *Chapter Seven* of this text.

Understanding the cause utilizes and integrates all three domains of healing. You can understand the decisions and circumstances that preceded the problem. Sometimes the cause stems from learned family patterns of behavior that for generations have been (unknowingly) breaking natural laws. Sometimes the problem relates to intense survival-based programming, when "little things" are made so important. Children replicate early models of behavior, affecting the rest of their lives.

By going to the cause behind the symptom, you are empowered to take responsibility for it, and quickly alleviate the cause. This approach empowers you to get well and most of all - stay committed to well-being!

Discovering a Way to Locate the Cause

For many years I successfully worked with patients only to have them return with the same or a similar problem later. This bothered me so much that I decided to focus on the possible root cause of their problem. Over the years, as I explored new methodologies and adapted new techniques, I had no consistent way to successfully find the underlying cause, although I consistently found myself ending up with an emotional pattern affecting their attitude.

After adding Muscle Response Testing[5] (MRT) to my practice, *The Cause* became much easier to discover. MRT allowed me to communicate with the body's hidden information. As I traced a problem to its cause, I often uncovered early childhood or core programming that was still causing reactionary behavior. A common example would be for a person to feel *rejection* or feel *"not good enough"* in some area of their life. While a certain amount of this is normal, most barriers to achievement are because of this kind of core programming that *"needs to be right"* about its hidden beliefs. Meaning that once the mind has made a decision such as "I'm not good enough," the mind will try to prove its decision is correct by looking at life from that viewpoint. The mind can unwittingly draw circumstances to itself to prove that what it believes is true or correct. Thus the mind re-creates (re-forms) its experience of life to support its perceived "unlovability" and "inadequacy." The mind can take a perfectly harmless situation and see threats where none exist.

We have all unintentionally abused our bodies and have fallen short of perfect health at some time or another. And yet, our bodies are "wonderfully made" to heal and repair themselves. Through symptoms, our bodies are

---

[5]Muscle Response Testing is the method of using a muscle to test your body at a cellular level to uncover hidden or subconscious information. (See Glossary)

telling us what is going on in the inner realms of the soul.[6] We are reminded through symptoms to seek the message behind them, learn our lesson, and move along.

If you hold on to resentments, guilt or anger, you block the natural flow of energy and bio-chemical fluids in the body. Then, very often you become further alienated from your body by getting angry with it for not working properly. People bring sickness upon themselves by the way they err in the laws of physical health, positive attitudes, and spiritual practices.

I love to see people healed as quickly as possible. It satisfies my soul. Though instant miraculous healings are wonderful, I love to see people understand the initial CAUSE–for with it comes compassion and love, "renewing their minds" and "transforming their lives." The potential limitation of receiving a miracle healing is that if the symptom is alleviated without healing the CAUSE, the problem may re-surface. It would then be necessary to repeat the healing. **Understanding** the underlying *Cause* and *aligning to the laws of health* creates cellular change, so the problem never returns. This can also appear like a miracle!

Physical Laws Regulate One's Body

Natural physical laws bring balance through proper nutrition, exercise, rest, and a healthy environment,

---

[6]Soul, represented in this text, is a combination of Mind, Will, and Emotions. (See glossary)

including being around happy, caring people. *Chapter Two* surveys these areas in more detail.

Many forms of healing fall into the category of physical laws, such as: Acupuncture, Allopathy (traditional western medicine), Chiropractic, Herbology, Homeopathy, Massage, Naturopathy, Osteopathy, Physical Therapy, Nutrition, etc. (See Glossary for descriptions.)

Although the above healing arts function primarily on the Physical Law level, many practitioners use psychological and spiritual practices to complement them. Vibrational medicine, which has been recently popularized, has linked the physical, electrical and etheric worlds to gain more understanding on hidden causes of diseases. Though we cannot see bioenergy, we can monitor it through specialized equipment and by the changes that take place in the physical realm. Electro-diagnostic devices have been developed for the purposes of diagnosing, monitoring and supporting the healing process. These machines are linked with Homeopathic Remedies, Bach Flower Essences, Radionics, Light Therapy, Sound Therapy and Aroma Therapy, all a part of vibrational medicine and described in the Glossary. I like what Dr. Richard Gerber, M.D.[7] said:

"Doctors are beginning to reconceptualize human beings as more than just bodies of flesh and bones.

---

[7]Author of *"Vibrational Medicine,"* 1988, Bear & Company.

They are beginning to understand that we possess unique energy systems that help to maintain health. "

The physical body can act as a barometer to let you know what is going on inside at deeper subconscious levels. Physical complaints act as "wake-up calls" to alert us to follow the natural laws of health, whether that be physical, mental, or spiritual. By the time you are aware of a problem on the physical plane it is time to truly listen. Imbalance shows up in the electrical field of the body first. To restrict treatment to the physical realm is to focus on the symptom, not the cause. Even frequent accidents can make us wonder if some subconscious decision may be involved. If you are not well physically or happy emotionally, the body will be your barometer; at first whispering, then shouting its message. Chronic pain is one sure way of knowing you are resisting the healing process by harboring old hurts and resentments.

If you have been in treatment for any problem more than a few weeks and are not improving, you need to look at *The Cause!* The body can heal from major surgery in a couple of weeks. So why are you still in your problem? The body is a wonderful repair shop, if given the chance.

Understanding the relationship of the symptom to the cause is powerful. This, in itself, can create the space for the miracle of healing to happen. Often healing begins when the cause is simply exposed. Rapid cellular change takes place as the brain sends messages to the body to repair as fast as possible. The healing process itself is a miracle, though usually not accepted as such, unless it happens rapidly. I believe that every healing has the miraculous in it - the miracle of NEW LIFE!

One lady came to me after suffering for over eight months with constant neck pain from an auto accident. She felt resentment and anger against the person who hit her. In a Kalos Process[8] she discovered how she helped create that accident to avoid facing the fear of being with her sister, whom she didn't want to face. After processing the incident and seeing "the truth" her pain miraculously left. She went on to heal the conflict with her sister.

Chapter Two of this text will give more on the physical laws of health, while Kalos Transformational Healing Book Three, *The Manual,* explores them further. It focuses especially on detailed testing for a complete wholistic physical examination. You will learn how to follow through with a balanced program for optimum well-being. However, since chronic problems universally have an underlying mental/emotional aspect, it is imperative that the *Kalos Process* in this book first be understood, then wisely applied.

Mental Precepts Direct One's Thinking

Natural laws govern our thoughts and feelings. I call them *precepts*. Mental Precepts help you understand the functioning of your mind and support your awareness to not get caught in the mind's survival programming. At the core, the mind's basic needs for survival are:

---

[8] What The Process is called, as taught in this text, see Glossary.

1. The left brain needs to be ACCURATE to survive.
2. The right brain needs to be ACCEPTED to survive.

This survival mechanism works well on a physical level, but on the psycho/emotional level it can create some major problems. For example, sickness can be a result of holding on to grudges and resentments for feeling unloved (a basic right brain need). Carrying unresolved emotional upsets (conscious or unconscious) can cause abnormal cellular activity (physical illness) or unusual behavior (mental illness). **Hence, the value of forgiveness**.

Grudges and resentments are based upon survival programming from drawing conclusions before all the evidence is in. *Anytime a decision is made with great emotion attached, it becomes the rule of action from that time forth.* Your mind automatically brings up reactions linked to the past, having little or nothing to do with what is happening now. Most judging results from past emotional experiences programmed when we were very young and in a **perpetration.**

> A perpetration is something you believe to be true that isn't; a type of deception you secretly hold (even from yourself), carrying extended consequences.

When the truth is known, you usually find your perceptions carried misunderstandings with them. Misperceiving for a child who is less equipped with knowing how to explore the full truth of a situation, is very understandable. However, these mis-perceptions can be carried over to adult years and affect behavior now! How you live each moment builds upon what has gone before; yet you always have choice. When "the truth" is known, you might even discover that forgiveness becomes unnecessary, because there is nothing left to forgive!

This happens when you deeply experience another's life and get insight into the positive intention behind their behavior. Seeing the full picture clearly can set you free from resentment and guilt. You go to the other side of forgiveness where love and compassion replaces anger, fear and guilt. An example of this is found in the story told in *"A new Day in Healing"* of the man with a dented new car, whose anger changed to compassion when he discovered the desperate motivation of the boy who threw the rock to save his brother's life. When the truth is known, a miracle takes place. A change of thought causes one's feelings to change. Changing feelings changes the chemical reaction within the body. Bringing one's body/mind to peace allows the natural healing powers of the body to do their best. I have even seen growths disappear in a matter of hours.

To renew the mind & permanently resolve the cause - fears and attitudes will need transforming.

Early in my healing work, I began asking questions to locate fears going on in people's lives. I wanted to see **if** and **how** the patient had created the problem. Many times patients told me of their frustrations, fears and insecurities.

19

This bore out my impressions that the root of their problem was at least 70 percent beyond the physical domain and came from their mental attitude.

This question arose within me: "How could people effectually change their core attitude?" This became my challenge. Attitudes develop and are reinforced over a long period. How could our little amount of time together make any difference at all? Many questions came into my mind as I decided to explore this new adventure. One thing I knew already: Spirit had made the biggest difference in my attitude.

Spiritual Principles to Bless Our Lives

Love is the greatest healer. The injunction to "love others as we love ourselves" was a mystery to me. I questioned how much I even loved myself, let alone love others. What I discovered was transforming. As a child of nine years old, I discovered that the more I was kind to others and served them, the happier I became. The result created more love for myself! Self love increased as I happily shared my love with others, giving me a sense of what it was like to be loved by God. Because of knowing God's love for me, I trusted that no matter what, everything resulted in a **benefit!** Even though life became challenging and sometimes painful, I could always count on a benefit to show up, because I was loved by a Universal God.

- My attitude uplifted to seeing the benefits in life, rather than obsessing on the shadow side.

- The more I acted out of the spiritual principles of love and trust, the more my attitude improved.
- I began to see the benefits in other people's lives too and how much everyone has to be grateful for.

Spiritual Principles are always operating in our lives. They are derived from the very essence of WHO we are. As you observe and surrender your busy mind to the way of peace and gratitude, you can experience them in operation. Just as your mind needs to be accurate and accepted to survive, spirit doesn't need anything. Spirit is eternal, cannot be destroyed, and the source of everything.

Unconditionally loving boggles the mind that wants an "eye for an eye" and a "tooth for a tooth." The mind wants fairness or retribution. And life isn't always fair (in the moment, that is). Spiritual principles go beyond mental programming, causing one to stretch one's consciousness into a more profound perception, fostering a new experience, which can be initially uncomfortable. Our minds, being logical and practical, want comfort; whereas, spirit may lead us into unknown paths of mystery and uncomfortable situations of exploration.

Everyone has conscious CHOICE. Choice is one of our special blessings for being human and gives us the option to determine how we respond out of our whole being in any situation. We can respond in love or react in fear. Choice makes the difference. We are challenged to trust that everyone is doing the best they can in the moment. Therefore, our job is to listen, support, evaluate and choose the most loving response. Of course, this type of action can "blow" the logic of a mind that needs to justify that action. The mind only accepts conditionally,

21

such as to love another only when that love is returned, and of course not to love an enemy. Genuine, unconditional loving is the realm of spirit.

Most people's problems are multidimensional, though *the Cause* often goes back into the subconscious programming where a principle of life has been tampered with. While most complaints are on the physical plane, looking at the possible mental, emotional or spiritual cause to alleviate the *real* problem is more than valuable. It is necessary. You can:

Heal the Body! Renew the Mind! Free the Spirit!

Three Choices to Make About your Problem

FIRST — **Make a clear decision to heal!**

SECOND — **Understand your problem on a causal level.** You can trace a problem back to its root cause using MRT (described in *Chapter Six*) and find out the specifics on how it began. As you study the Laws, Precepts and Principles in this text, you will understand how, when and where you went out of balance and what to do about it.

THIRD — **Take responsibility, acknowledge, and align your relationship to any natural law that relates to your problem.** You have a wonderful opportunity to explore new possibilities for your health and happiness by aligning yourself to the Laws, Precepts and Principles described herein.

22

Are you willing to look at the cause of the problem and resolve it, making restitution[9] when appropriate? The clearer you understand the cause, the more your faith grows into perfect action and results. <u>Are you willing to align yourself to the natural laws of health</u>? Are you willing to do what you can to take care of yourself, and trust God's grace to do the rest? Faith is still the healer and is increasingly actuated as you understand the cause of your ailment and align yourself to the appropriate law.

Be open to the possibility that YOU can make the decision to heal. If you have a long-term problem, you can be sure that somewhere, on some level, there is a subconscious decision NOT to be healed. Deep feelings of unworthiness or strong beliefs that healing is impossible may be sending a message throughout your body. You may have a hidden belief that if you get well you will have to do something that you cannot avoid, because you can't say "no" without a "proper" reason. Whatever it is, you can break into this negative cycle and set yourself free. It begins by opening to the possibility that God loves you and wants you well!

The Wheel of Health *(Chapter Five)* will support you to look at what area of your life could use transforming. Transformational Healing is just as much about transforming your life into a full potential of joy as it is about healing a specific ailment. Everyone is meant to have a full potential reason to live!

---

[9]Restitution (Glossary) To restore losses or compensate for damages one has incurred against another.

Highlights

- Natural Laws govern the healing process. It is the breaking of these laws that cause disease.

- The three realms of Transformational Healing comprise:

  1. Physical Laws
  2. Mental Precepts
  3. Spiritual Principles

- The Law of Cause and Effect is always in operation. Life is continually seeking and creating balance.

- Physical ailments are simply the body's way of trying to adjust or compensate to maintain perfect balance.

- Transformational Healing grants us the ability to understand WHY we got the problem in the first place.

- You can learn to trace any problem to its cause, whether physical, mental or spiritual.

- Your beliefs affect the healing process. Wanting to live is necessary to wanting to be well.

- We bring sickness upon ourselves by the way we err in the laws of physical health, positive attitudes, and spiritual practices.

- Natural physical laws bring balance through proper nutrition, exercise, rest and a healthy environment, including being around happy, caring people.

- Mental Precepts expose how the mind might ironically interfere with your health through its programmed need for survival:

  1. Left brain needs to be accurate to survive.
  2. Right brain needs to be accepted to survive.

- A perpetration is something you believe to be true that isn't; a type of deception.

- Your core attitude toward life accounts for about 70% of your health.

- Spiritual Principles uncover the hidden laws of spiritual empowerment - Unconditional love and trust.

- Knowing there is an unidentified law behind every problem opens the door to finding what that law is to restore balance.

- Ask yourself these questions:
  1. Are you open to understand the cause?
  2. Are you open to experiment with aligning to the natural law that was broken?
  3. Are you open to trust?
  4. Are you open to being healed?

Participant's Page

1. Write down some goals or projects you would like to understand and gain results with while studying this text.

   A.

   B.

   C.

2. After reading this text once, invite a friend to go through it with you and participate in the methodologies.

3. Make arrangements to observe and experience Muscle Response Testing (MRT).

Chapter Two

Aligning with Physical Laws

A Growth Disappears

When I was seventeen years old, a growth formed on my eyelid which became very sore to touch. After weeks of thinking it would go away, I went to the eye doctor to see what was wrong. I was told it was a chalazion (a type of cyst) and that the only way I could get rid of it was by surgery. So I agreed and went through a very painful operation and recovery.

Several years later, the chalazion regrettably returned (not surprising, since I never understood and resolved the cause). This time I was a student of health and wanted to understand WHY it happened so I could get rid of it permanently. Even with all my studies, I had no idea what could have caused this terrible growth. I only knew I did not want to go through that surgical ordeal again and was informed that was the only recourse known. Feeling that only God knew why the growth was there (as this happened before I learned MRT), I prayed daily to understand the cause. After about two months of praying, while the chalazion was becoming larger, I awoke one morning and the answer flashed before my eyes — SUGAR! What a shock! Arguing with the answer, I felt confused because I didn't eat sugar very often. I never even kept sugar in my cupboards at home. The next answer I received was that it was not only regular sugar, it was also the sugar in foods, like the dried apricots I had been eating regularly. A light went on in my head as I realized that I used quite a bit of honey and loved sweet fruits, too. I even took the children out for ice cream cones almost weekly. So, although I didn't use plain white sugar in my home, I was getting too much sugar from other foods, especially the apricots, which I dried from our tree.

Now that I understood the problem, I prayed for direction to resolve it. The answer I received was to stop all sugar and sweet foods for one month. I committed myself to do this and was amazed to discover that in less than a week the soreness on my eyelid was gone. By the end of the month the growth had completely disappeared!

This example of healing, by resolving the underlying cause, became the focus of my practice. Though both methods (surgery and not eating sugar) could get rid of the chalazion, the second method was painless and brought an understanding so that I could prevent any recurrence. I broke a natural law which threw my body out of chemical balance. All the sugars I was eating, though mainly natural, upset this chemical balance. Only by understanding the law I was breaking, could I be responsible for taking care of my body in a meaningful way. The surgeon's knife was quick, but painful. The natural way took longer because the problem was longstanding. However, often, when problems are caught in the early stages, the healing process can be more rapid than waiting for a surgery date. Also, my discovery of the natural law I was breaking enabled me to protect myself from having high blood sugar (diabetes), which could have been much worse than the chalazion. And best of all, I never need to be concerned with the problem returning!

Laws Govern the Healing Process

Natural Laws are always in operation. There is an answer to every problem. My chalazion story happened before I learned Applied Kinesiology[10] and a way of using Muscle Response Testing to identify causes. Therefore, I was unable to test the cause of my problem directly, as can be done today. I had to rely solely upon hearing an answer to prayer. Sometimes it takes a while to hear the voice of the Spirit. And then, I even argued with my guidance because of my lack of understanding of natural laws.

Could ignorance be the reason why overeating sweets is such a serious problem in our society? I am astounded at the amount of people with an imbalance of blood sugar, and even who are allergic to sugar. Without realizing it, people's life styles are breaking the laws of health on a daily basis. Aligning oneself to the "Laws of Health" requires a focused commitment. Shifting old habits is a major part of the healing process. *When I understood the*

---

[10]Applied Kinesiology a form of Muscle Response Testing.
(See Glossary for detailed explanation.)

cause of how to resolve my chalazion problem, I no longer had any fear of its return.

The Law of Cause and Effect Is Always in Operation

Like our planetary system, our bodies are always functioning to keep us in balance. Adjustments and compensations go on continually to maintain the most perfect balance possible. Ailments that arise are simply the body's way of adjusting or compensating to maintain perfect balance. By understanding and aligning to the laws operating within your body, mind, and spirit, you can bring rapid healing. Maybe all disease is the effect of your body doing what it can to balance and preserve your life. As an example, the body will even wall off toxic substance to keep it from damaging a vital organ.

You are programmed to heal. You never have to tell your body to heal a cut; it does it naturally. The same goes for the other parts. When a cut does not heal, we want to know the cause. Though medical science has told us that diabetics don't heal very easily because of the high blood sugar, it has not told us how to prevent diabetes. Have you ever wondered why we never hear about what really causes high blood sugar? Yet, diabetes is one of the fastest growing diseases and contributes to a myriad of other ailments in civilized nations.

We are more interested in the WHY of a problem, because we want to permanently heal and not ever have that problem again. Hence, we offer you many possible places that you can look for *The Cause*.

Healing does not need to be difficult. The body may be intricately complex, but it functions by simple laws and principles. Our mind may also be complex, but it functions in a simple way too. Healing can be as uncomplicated as aligning oneself to the *laws of health*. Though I am not going into very much detail on the physical laws of health in this text, I am offering a few basic concepts for your understanding and alignment.

The Physical Aspect to Health

The basic *physical* components for health are:

1. Nutrition (with proper combining and preparing of whole foods, supplements and herbs)
2. Detoxification and cleanse (tissue, blood, lymph, bowels)
3. Regular exercise (stretch, walk, aerobic, etc.)
4. Proper rest and relaxation (daily, weekly, seasonally)
5. Pollution Free Environment (clean air, pure water, happy caring people, etc.)

1. Get Honest with Nutrition

Foods can be remedies for many ailments, or they can be a factor in the cause of your problem. Food is fuel to replenish energy in your body. It accomplishes this in at least three ways:

1) Building
2) Repairing
3) Eliminating or Cleansing

Protein and starch are the building blocks of the body. They work with minerals and vitamins to build and repair body tissue, organs and cells. Building and repairing is an ongoing process. Certain alkaline forming proteins, that are found in foods such as nuts and dairy products, become altered in the heating or cooking process and can cause a toxic condition in the body affecting the lymph glands, sinuses, ears, etc. Dr. Francis Pottenger's[11] research clearly showed how cooked protein caused severe defects in cats by the third generation. The proteins used in his 10 year study on more than 900 cats were essentially meat and dairy.

Many toxic conditions, such as arthritis, kidney disease, lymphatic congestion, premature aging, etc. arise from eating too many acid forming foods and too little live enzymes. The heating of protein destroys the natural enzymes that nature places there and changes the alkaline proteins to acid forming proteins in the system. Raw milk is alkaline forming in your system, whereas pasteurized milk is acid forming, as are cheeses, yogurt, etc. Most

---

[11]Dr. Francis M. Pottenger, American Journal of Orthodontics and Oral Surgery, August 1946.

nuts are altered in the roasting process into acid forming compounds.

I am not saying that you can never use cooked protein. I am saying that to become well from an over acid condition or a toxic protein related problem may require you to dramatically adjust your diet. Balance is the key! Dr. Bernard Jensen[12] says that the best ratio is 20% acid forming foods to 80% alkaline forming foods.

Use more raw and sprouted foods. Acid forming grains change into an alkaline forming food when sprouted.

Are We Becoming a Drugged Society?

It takes five feet of sugar cane to make three teaspoons of sugar. White sugar is similar to a drug, yet is added to almost every processed food at the grocery store! Among the side effects of refined sugar is the leaching of calcium and other valuable nutrients from your body, which can leave you with nutritional deficiencies. Diabetes is so common today that many pregnant women are asked to take the sugar tolerance test to avoid complications.

Refined and processed foods are depleting our vital energy that is needed by our immune system. Stop using them and your general health will improve, especially your eyes, teeth and gum conditions. Almost every chronic inflammatory condition will improve with stopping the

---

[12]Dr. Bernard Jensen, D.C., N.D., a leading nutritionist, who has pioneered natural healing.

intake of white sugar (sucrose). Sometimes discontinuing the eating of a debilitating food is necessary to gain optimum health (as I did to heal the chalazion in my eyelid), rather than adding something nutritious to your diet.

White flour products are not only found to be deficient through the refining process, but they rob your body of valuable nutrients. They require the same vitamins and minerals that are in the whole grain to digest properly. Especially the B Vitamins become deficient, which are required for mental processing and coping with stress. Hyperactive children are found to be very deficient in the B vitamins. According to research, the only vitamins that can increase your learning ability are the B-complex. Over twenty-seven vitamins and minerals are removed from wheat when refined, while only five to seven synthetics replace them. How is it they call this enriched?

Depleted processed foods, food additives, chemical colorings, drugs, synthetic vitamins and minerals, and unnatural fertilizers are introducing foreign substances into our bodies. We are ingesting over one million substances today that were not in our diets less than 100 years ago. We are having to adapt to a new environment to survive our modern way of living. We must rethink what we put into our bodies, because synthetics have become the rule. All of these potentially new considerations in what and how you eat may seem complex. What is most encouraging is that you won't need an advanced degree in nutrition to eat right. I am suggesting a few simple rules to start observing. More on nutrition with a complete list of foods and their nutrients are listed in Book Three of this series, *"The Manual."*

2. Detoxification and Cleanse

Fruits and Vegetables Are Great Cleansers

Fruits and vegetables not only work with protein to build body tissue, they also are important for the proper acid - alkaline balance. Used in a cleansing program, raw fruits and vegetables break down toxins and flush out unwanted acids and poisons from the cells. Fruits stir up toxins (poisons) in the body, while non-starchy vegetables work like a broom to sweep them out. The fewer the starches and proteins, the more the cleansing effect. Raw green vegetables have a special cleansing effect by breaking down the toxic waste to a smaller molecule, making it easier for the body to eliminate. The green chlorophyll in vegetables is anti-inflammatory and helps the body heal faster. I love what Dr. Jensen used to say, "If you're green inside, you're clean inside!"

Raw vegetable juices and "green drinks" are some of the best nourishers and healers, as they are anti-inflammatory and have the enzymes that speed up the cleansing process. These drinks are easily made with inexpensive Juicers available in health food stores and in most department stores. They can assist you in doing a beautiful job in cleansing your body. A wonderful combination for cleansing the blood is carrot, celery and cucumber juice. Some parsley added will give you more chlorophyll, calcium and iron. This same combination works well for inflammation of the veins and blood clots. Spring and summer are the best times of the year to cleanse, unless you have mild winters. Use less cucumber juice in cold weather.

For a chlorophyll cocktail (green drink) it is best to use a blender and place in leafy greens such as chard, spinach, kale, parsley, etc. and liquefy with fresh pineapple, water and/or diluted pineapple juice. Drink plenty of water on a cleanse to flush your system. Anyone can go on a one to five day cleanse on their own. For longer cleanses, please consult with a health professional.

Use fruits with caution on a cleansing program, as many people with health problems in our day have an imbalance in their blood sugar or Candida Albicans (a fungus) and cannot tolerate fruits. The use of Muscle Response Testing, introduced in *Chapter Six*, will allow you to know exactly which foods to use during a cleansing and maintenance program. Never use table salt on a cleanse. In fact, you would do well to eliminate it completely.

Relax and trust your body to know how to cleanse and heal itself. Get professional assistance if you have severe toxicity. Don't worry! Worry affects the pancreas the most, so *relax and do your best* on a cleanse! Trust your body to heal and repair itself.

Herbs Are Wonderful Cleansers, Healers and Repairers

Herbs contain a concentration of nutrients and have a special way of going to the exact place in the body needing help. There are cleansing herbs, energizing herbs, and building herbs. Many medications originated from herbs. Because of the medicinal qualities of some herbs, you will be better served to consult for professional advice when using them as medicines.

Specific cleanses for different parts of your body are covered in the third book of this series, *"The Manual,"* including cleanses for the colon, lymph, organs, tissue, etc.

3. Exercise for Health and Fitness!

Start an Exercise Program Today
You Know it! Just Do It.

There are many types of exercises to choose from. At least begin an exercise program by walking briskly daily. When you are walking at least twelve minutes a day for two weeks, you then can lengthen the time until you feel your energy level increasing. Never jog or run without first walking for at least two weeks. Gradually work into a more vigorous program like alternating between walking and jogging with proper professional advice. (Running is not recommended with excess weight or knee or ankle weakness.)

Preceding your walks or jogs with stretching exercises relaxes your muscles and prevents soreness and strains. Warm up by stretching and cool down by adding one to three minutes of slow exercise.

Twelve minutes of aerobic exercise is recommended daily for optimum health. If you are unable to do very active exercise, at least do stretch and dynamic tension exercises. You can gradually work up to an aerobic program. There are many types that may suit you: stretching, water aerobics, biking, hiking, etc. There are specific exercises you can do to benefit different parts of your body, such as back exercises to strengthen and eliminate pain.

Muscle Response Testing can be used to see how much exercise is your optimum at any given time. You already know how good you feel when getting the proper exercise. Be honest with yourself. A regular exercise program will keep you feeling young and fit, building your self-esteem. You may find that you do best when someone else exercises with you. Many people want to enjoy the beauties of nature while exercising, rather than be inside on mechanical equipment. However you are drawn, make sure you really enjoy it. Make it as fun as possible!

Running is a quick rejuvenater. When I need to increase my energy quickly, I run. When I am functioning on little sleep, because of a busy traveling and teaching schedule, short vigorous exercise feels great! A ten minute run seems to clear my mind and rejuvenate my strength. Two or three minutes of vigorous exercise can also make a difference. Be sure to send out loving thoughts and gratitude while running. Pray, praise, and bless people. Your attitude will support your energy level immensely.

4. Are You Getting the Proper Rest?

Our bodies require the proper rest to rejuvenate. Mostly, our nervous system needs to stop and relax. Most adults require from six to eight hours of sleep a night. I am amazed at how little sleep people require when in good health, usually only five to six hours nightly, depending upon their stress level.

Meditation makes a big difference in my ability to rejuvenate my body and mind quickly by allowing my body to completely relax. A few minutes can be as energizing as an hour of sleep. To master the art of meditation is to give you more valuable waking hours. Meditation can begin your day with heightened awareness and clarity as to how to spend your day the most effectively. You become attuned in body, mind and spirit. Meditation can also prepare you for sleep, dissipating tensions and dispelling turbulent thoughts that interfere with deep levels of relaxation. You can realign your purpose and enter a joyful state.

Meditation is about being still and listening, and does not require long periods of time. A few minutes a day (15 minutes) can make a surprising difference. Frequent short light meditations of 2 to 5 minutes are preferred by some in place of longer periods of deeper meditative states. However you choose to include meditation in your life is up to you. My recommendation is that you stop running from "the silence," but embrace it fully. Meditation will support you to respond to life's stressful situations in a peaceful, full potential way.

It's not the stress that's hard on you, it's your response to it!

Stop! Breathe! Remember: The more your body can relax the faster it can rejuvenate. Relax and remember to "give thanks in all things." Then, look for the benefit! Stop making little frustrations into big ones. A proven method of up-scaling your work productivity is to take a longer lunch break. You will do much better to relax, clear your mind and then go back to your mental or physical labors.

Giving yourself the proper exercise and rest will increase your ability to express love. You stop being up-tight with others and give them more space to be themselves. Along with rest comes relaxation. Playful recreation can re-create your relationship into joyful experiences. Marriages are enhanced by taking one weekend a month to a "get away." How long has it been since you have enjoyed a two week vacation? When children get up-tight and irritable, we do not hesitate to say, "Take time out." What about us parents? Maybe taking time out is just what is needed in such a demanding world. Take a vacation just for the Health of it! You deserve it!

5. A Clean Environment

A recent report published by the United States government shows that almost half the cities in the U.S. have pollutants beyond safe limits in their water supply.

Every household could benefit from a water filtering system.

Free-radicals[13] are embedding themselves within our bodies and damaging the DNA of the cells. Chlorination of our water supply, exhaust fumes from our automobiles, pasteurization of dairy products, chemical additives to our food supplies, cigarette smoking and much more are causing free radical related diseases to skyrocket. This is contributing to our nation's number one cause of death, cardiovascular disease, as well as cancer (the second largest cause of death) and many other problems.

Today, as never before, pollution has reached such proportions that many believe its effects cannot be changed in time for the long-term survival of the human race. Drinking contaminated water, breathing polluted air, ingesting drugs and chemicals, eating denatured, processed foods and living a stressful life have surely taken their toll. Environmental disease has become a major threat in our day with more and more people having to live limited lives, imprisoned away from pollutants.

Electromagnetic radiation is affecting our body's and brain's electrical system, as well as contributing to free-radical based diseases. You can obtain some of the research I did several years ago by sending for my booklet: *How To Protect Yourself From Electromagnetic Radiation* (order form on last page of this book).

Our high standard of living has brought along with it man-made radiation in the form of television sets, microwave ovens, fluorescent lights, battery operated watches, computer screens and electronics of all sorts.

---

[13]Free radicals are non-ionic compounds, free flowing, highly reactive, in which the central element is linked to an abnormal number of atoms or groups of atoms. (Blakinston's Medical Dictionary)

Everywhere we go our environment is polluted to such a degree, it is imperative we keep our attitude positive and our immune system strong.

Examining all of these areas in our lives will help us see where we can improve. Are we doing all we can to support wellness for ourselves and others? It is time to put aside greed and focus on preserving the well-being of the human race. If we think that we can wait around for someone else to come and take us out of this contaminated state, think again. As a people, it is time to put our priorities in order and focus on some real threats to us all by being loving stewards of planet earth. In so doing, we can improve the quality of personal life, health, and well-being for all. I appreciate the innovations and conferences around the world committed to cleaning up our environment — I heartily give my thanks!

Highlights

- Laws govern the healing process. There is an answer to every problem.

- The law of cause and effect is always in operation. Our bodies are always functioning to keep us in balance.

- The basic *physical* components for health are:
  1. Nutrition
  2. Detoxification and cleanse
  3. Regular exercise
  4. Proper rest
  3. Pollution Free Environment

- Food as fuel replenishes energy in your body allowing three major functions to be accomplished: building, repairing, and eliminating or cleansing.

- Eat more raw and sprouted food. A toxic condition can arise when too many acid forming foods or heated proteins are ingested.

- Refined and processed foods are depleting your vital energy needed by your immune system, especially refined sugar. Stop using them!

- Fruits and vegetables are cleansing foods. Fruits stir up the toxins, while vegetables work like a broom and sweep them out.

- Herbs have innate properties that go to particular areas in the body to build, repair and regenerate.

- Exercise gives your body the circulation needed to get proper oxygen and nutrients to all the cells, especially the brain. Start an exercise program today!

- The proper amount of rest and vacations are needed for optimum health, including our health in careers and relationships.

- Meditation can make a big difference in the amount of sleep you require.

- It's not the stress that's hard on you. It's your response to it! Stop! Breathe! Relax and give thanks!

- Today, as never before, pollution has reached alarming proportions. Almost 50% of the drinking water in the U.S. is reported by a government agency to be contaminated.

- Environmental disease has become a major threat with more people having to live limited lives away from pollutants.

Participant's Page

1. Pick an area of your physical well-being that you commit to focus upon for the next 30 days, such as to stop all white sugar, and **promise** yourself to keep that commitment. You may choose to go on a cleanse for a day or more. This would entail discontinuing eating proteins and starches and eating only non-starchy vegetables and fruits. Of course, you want to drink lots of water. Vegetable juices are great cleansers. Be sure to get professional assistance if you cleanse over five days or have a physical ailment.

2. List some ways to clean up your environment and set a time when each will be accomplished. Be sure to include a water filtering system, if you need one.

3. Create an exercise program that you enjoy. Aerobic exercises are recommended for a minimum of three times per week. Precede with stretching and warm up exercises and end with cool downs.

Chapter Three

Mental Precepts

Our minds are made of millions of bits of multi-dimensional affective information, including our thoughts and feelings. The mind, though nonphysical, is an essential part of our physical functioning, for it controls our physical bodies. Mental Precepts help you understand the natural functioning of the mind.

The mind is a complete library of everything that has ever happened to us. This library is called programming.

Science estimates that over 80 percent of our present behavior stems from what has been programmed from the past. Information stored in our memory banks affects our attitude and all aspects of our life; therefore our health. The mind is programmed for our survival. Every decision the mind makes is to protect us and keep us:

Safe - physically
Correct (right, proper, justified) - mentally
Accepted - emotionally

What a wonderful servant! How supportive to know that working for us twenty-four hours a day is a mind longing for our comfort - automatically! There is only one problem. *The mind would rather be safe and right than happy.* Some of our greatest experiences are when we choose to do the daring or the dangerous. With a mind always running from discomfort you might ask, "How can one grow?"

Growing is not the problem. Growth happens! You need not be concerned. What I am inviting you to re-access is: "Are you 'running from' any area of your life, rather than 'choosing to' do what is the most enlivening?" "Running from" has no satisfaction in it. Our problem is not how the mind is programmed for survival. Our problem stems from giving up CHOICE. The key to mastering the mind is to let it be your SERVANT, not your master.

Your Mind Works Automatically; Therefore, It is a Wonderful Servant, but a Terrible Master

Notice how much of your behavior is automatic, running like a machine. Have you noticed when someone pushes your button, you react? Reacting to situations, rather than responding to life in-the-moment, can cause needless struggles. The truth is: *You are not your programming;* you have conscious CHOICE. You have the power to take charge of your mental programming and make it your servant. A servant does not make your choices for you, but supports you in carrying out those choices. Only you can **think**, **choose** and **act** for yourself; otherwise, your mind will take over and do what is automatically the most comfortable, not the most loving. You always have a choice. When emotions rule you, it's like the tail wagging the dog. The power and ability to choose are yours - servant or master?

The Mind Only Functions from Its Programming

The mind can only function in the past (gone and cannot be changed), or in the future (an illusion). Spirit functions in the present moment, NOW. Now is an eternal place, outside time. In the "eternal moment" you make choices out of the essence of WHO you are. If you find yourself making choices you don't like, look at the possibility of your mind taking automatic control, instead of being your servant.

CHOICE only takes place when there are at least two different alternatives without an emotional backed need pulling you in a certain direction. For instance, if your mind has a NEED to be right or an intensified feeling for one choice over another, I would not consider this a choice at all. I would consider this way of deciding an emotional compulsion in the mind's programming. Needs are usually based upon fear. Therefore, anytime you are feeling an emotional fear without a real threat, notice if your mind is running your decision, not you.

Though your mind is masterful at storing information, what is happening now may not be the same as what the mind thinks happened in the past. The two may not be relative, though your feelings may be the same. Your mind can confuse situations to be the same when the same feelings come up. This is why unless you stay conscious in the present moment you will not be able to discern what those differences are. As an example, if you had a painful experience in a relationship in the past, the mind will bring up the same associated fear, as it did in the past when the same loving feelings come up. Feelings become attached to each other like the barnacles on a rock. Even opposing feelings like love and hate become connected in response/reaction to someone or something.

Your mind continually works for your comfort and safety. Just remember, you are not your mind. You are far more. Let your mind be your servant, remembering you always have choice. As soon as you discover you are being run around by your programming, you are not! Choice becomes an option when you are aware of what is happening, when it is happening. You become the happy observer!

Choice, though often uncomfortable, gives you an experience of being "in charge" of your life. You get to own your life as a leader, instead of being led around by your emotions. You will experience the JOY of self-mastery as you live by the Spirit now, and now, and now. Do not be hard on yourself. As you practice more on surrendering to the present moment, inner knowing becomes easier. You will increasingly find yourself humbled by the awesomeness of being led by Spirit.

The Mind Must Be "Right" to Survive

In order for your mind to stay functioning well, it must act as if it is right. Though later it may decide that it was not, in that very moment of decision, it was. The mind must be accurate to survive! When the mind is in charge, not under a physical addiction, everything the mind does is to be RIGHT, PROPER, OR JUSTIFIED or it cannot do it! Of course, if physical addictions rule your life, your body does not function in the same way. The "flesh" doesn't care how justified or right you are. It only wants immediate physical satisfaction (physical rightness). This is functioning "out of your mind" and results in self-defeating behavior - a dingbat role. Fortunately, most of the time the mind controls the body.

Explore your life through this perspective and you will discover what I mean. Think of a time that you did something that later you wished you hadn't done. Now, think of how you justified or thought it was right at the exact moment of doing it. Time after time I have found that in every case, even when the act was a crime, that the person thought he was right or at least justified.

The mind would even prefer being right rather than being happy. So, if your mind is fixated upon being right, it gets labeled self-righteous, causing you to be ineffective in ruling your life by the Spirit. Others say they prefer being safe rather than being happy. This shows their survival mechanism is working well, but at the expense of exploring new avenues of joy in living. As your mind seeks to make the new way right and support its new belief

51

to do the "right thing," you have another opportunity to experiment again. Every day is an opportunity to experiment at being all you can be, whether comfortable or not.

It is when you experiment with life, risking some comfort, that you enjoy the excitement of being alive! You can experience richer qualities of being that spur you on to living your purpose in a deeply meaningful way and risking to express that purpose dynamically in our world.

Beware!
Your Mind Has Three Tormentors

The mind, in seeking to keep us safe (accepted and right), instead can keep us in mental turmoil and emotional bondage. The mind constantly poses three doubts:

1. *Did I do the right thing?*
2. *Am I doing the right thing?*
3. *Will I do the right thing?*

In the mind's need to question every thought and action (past, present and future), it is only wanting to keep one safe and comfortable. Wanting to do the right thing is valuable for growth and not the real problem. The problem is: YOUR MIND MAKES WHATEVER IS COMFORTABLE, THE RIGHT THING TO DO.

I am grateful to have a mind that is looking out for my comfort and safety. As my servant, my mind serves me well. Nevertheless, as in the following story, when my mind seeks to master me, it gets in the way of my aliveness, my inner wisdom - the Spirit.

Once in the early morning, while praying about what Spirit wanted of me that day, I was directed to go to a certain woman's home who had been very ill. I had heard about this lady from her daughter only a few days before. She had severe migraine headaches and spent much of her time in bed. My mind did not want to follow Spirit's direction and go see her because of the discomfort about what she would think of me. After all, I didn't know her and offering my services to someone in this manner is not professional. My mind had all kinds of reasons why I should not go. Instead of being driven by my mind's need for comfort, I decided to call her and let her know that I was coming by to see her.

After arriving at her home, I told her I was asked to come and see her in my morning prayer and meditation. I felt moved to tell her that she did not have to stay ill, but could be healed. I told her what I believed was causing her migraines and gave her a diet to follow. She followed it exactly and called after a couple of weeks. When she returned from a trip, she said, "For the first time I can remember, I have gone on a trip without a headache and without a box of candy!" She went on to tell me how grateful she was to understand the *cause* of her migraines that had kept her in bed 2 or 3 days a week. She now felt FREE!

This story was a growth experience for me. I am grateful that I did not allow the fears and discomforts of my mind to keep me from following my inner guidance. For many years her annual Christmas card reminded me of her gratitude. What are YOU willing to experiment with, in following inner guidance?

The Fundamental Question of Aliveness

This question boggles the mind because its outcome is unknown:

"What am I Willing to Experiment With?"

An experiment is never right or wrong. It just is, and you always get the result. The mind wants to have all of the information in its memory banks in advance to be safe and comfortable. Experiments move outside the conditioned mind that looks for safety in the familiar. Seeing life as an experiment gives you opportunity to explore without judgment and expand valuable growth. As our servant, the mind's caution helps us avoid unnecessary pain. As our master, the mind keeps us in a rut of old familiar patterns and limitations, which it believes it needs for our comfort.

Sometimes, one feels uneasy stepping into a new situation, like a new career or a new relationship. Exploring new ways is how we expand and grow. Patterns of behavior, which feel comfortable eventually, may become dysfunctional, like a root bound potted plant stunted in its growth. So, stop worrying about your comfort. Your mind will take care of that for you. Instead, "What are you willing to experiment with?"

Thoughts and Feelings Affect Your Health

Healthy self-esteem is part of a healthy attitude and is a natural motivator to take better care of yourself. Inward guilt can cause self-condemnation and suppress the immune system. I have seen examples where viruses have been invited in because of guilt-ridden self punishment or a need to prove unworthiness.

Your Mind Functions under a False Purpose for Living

The mind functions on the assumption that your purpose for living is to be non-disturbed. This is why it approaches life in a defensive way, or you might say, "The road of least resistance." This is where the paradox comes in. In the mind's desire for comfort it can lose sight of the ultimate result - your joy. **Resisting** conflict and discomfort causes more of the same. Whatever we resist persists. Therefore, it can act in direct opposition to what it actually wants - a peaceful life. Your mind can function in opposition to what you actually want.

To the mind, safe means comfortable. The most comfortable time for the mind is when all of our cultural beliefs, family beliefs and personal beliefs overlap. This comfort zone becomes threatened when we step out into new arenas of living. This is why the mind is threatened by the thought of experimenting with something new. A significant mind threatening area is a career. Here intimidation can be experienced easily because others are watching. In trying to keep us safe, the mind can sabotage success in any area through fear of change, fear of acceptance, fear of failure and even fear of success.

Another major arena of sabotage is relationships. The mind may want to keep you uncommitted or distant to avoid intimacy. To open your heart in love is to open to the possibility of being rejected and hurt - something the mind prefers not risking, something very uncomfortable.

Inner spiritual guidance can intercept your fear and direct you, not only in relationships, but in every area of your life. So in your mind's desperate need for safety, it can lead you to the only truly secure place - the realm of Spirit, trusting all will be fine.

Your Mind Is Never Satisfied —
Always Wanting More, Better and Different!

Your mind automatically wants more, better and different to support you to evolve or achieve (intellectual comfort). This creates a paradox to wanting everything to be the same (emotional comfort). So, though you are satisfied one moment, the next one you're not! Watch your mind and notice your feelings. The act of observing the mind in action places you in charge again. Observing your mind's need for *more*, *better* and *different*, keeps you from being driven by that kind of programming.

Notice that when "more, better, different" becomes your emotionally driven force, you are at the effect of your programming. Noticing this releases you to make a new choice. The mind's discontent can cause stomach and bowel problems, including ulcers. The mind is never satisfied and is always "on guard" to protect us. Spirit, the observer, is contented with life, discerning benefits beyond the circumstances. Just acknowledging there is something of which to be grateful, the anxious mind can then relax and do its best. As we increasingly observe the mind, the mind increasingly serves us.

You Can Watch Your Mind in Action!

We are NOT our minds. We are far more than our programming. WE ARE SPIRIT, created in the image of God, with all the attributes of God. We can be in charge of our minds in a dynamic way. Each can be the master of their mind, instead of a victim of it. The following exercise can help you observe your mind in action and experience who **you** are.

Relax in a chair and don't think of anything; just be there with yourself, not thinking, only being still. Notice how the mind has difficulty being still. Notice how much of a busybody it is, always chattering. Patiently watching, you will notice it slowing down. One good way to do this exercise is while looking into another person's eyes and just being there, doing nothing. The same thing usually happens. The busy mind doesn't want to be still. It wants to do something constantly. Your mind is always looking out for your welfare, wanting your comfort. It is uncomfortable for you to do nothing, so it looks for something to do. The inner conversation you hear, the automatic evaluator and analyzer, is part of the functioning of your mind.

Practice this until you are freely observing your mind. You will discover WHO you are! YOU ARE THE ONE

OBSERVING! You are the one that chooses to speak or be still. You are the one in charge of your mind through observation and choice!

Every Time You Don't Feel Love and Peace
A Perpetration Is Involved

A perpetration is a lie or secret deception that you believe about yourself; such as, "I am not good enough" or "I am not loved." Perpetrations are hidden beliefs based upon an untruth. Since the mind made this (false) decision, it must prove it is right by creating an experience to justify itself. Most present time behavior is from past time programming, proving the mind to be right about what it believes is true. *(See Book One, A New Day in Healing, Chapter Ten, Playing the Perpetration Game.)*
During my earliest research, I spent two months tracing every negative feeling to its source. Much to my surprise, I discovered how <u>every</u> negative emotion had a perpetration attached. Often, my feelings were traced to a very young age when I feared rejection. My belief then was that I had to play a role of not disturbing anyone. Deeper yet, I discovered a decision I made when I was very young, "I am not loved." This laid the groundwork for needing to compensate for that decision by doing what I could to be loved, even if it meant to lie. I discovered how often I made excuses or told half truths, withholding information to protect myself from being rejected. Looking back (as a "normal" child), I saw how often I played out my deceptive belief of not being loved.

Running from one scenario to another, still my programming went with me - always proving "I am not loved." How strange the way the mind goes about proving it is right, even by setting up failures.

The mind begins to interpret everything as evidence to support its belief. Justifications are encrusted upon one another to bolster the (false) decision. Every feeling that is not founded on love has a perpetration behind it. Something hidden is going on. The Kalos Process can help you be the detective and discover the truth.

During upsets, perpetrations arise secretly to rule one's behavior to protect one's life. My early patterns came from my need to escape the pain of not feeling loved or not feeling good enough. Gaining comfort is a challenge while being driven by a fear filled mind - the fear of not being loved.

I found that every time I was not in a loving, harmonious place, I was in a perpetration. So now, when I am feeling less than a loving, peaceful state, I can look at the possibility of a perpetration being attached to it. Remembering how my mind is programmed to believe that *the purpose of living is to be non-disturbed*, I look within to make my decisions, not through fear, but through love.

Perpetrations form from premature judgments (drawing a conclusion before all of the evidence is in). Therefore, you can go beyond this negative repetitious cycle by stopping judging. When you notice yourself becoming defensive to justify thoughts or actions, it is a sign that you are emotionally attached to being right. A judgment, arising from this emotional attachment, causes a perpetration to take over, instead of you being in charge of your mind. As an example: "Dad doesn't love me because he screamed at me" was a false assumption made from Dad's yelling. I felt hurt. My mind decided, "I am not loved or Dad would have spoken kindly to me." That's a perpetration!

When a decision is made with intense emotion attached, a pattern is created from that time forth.

When someone you love (like Dad) raises a voice at you, it can bring up the old pattern of believing you are not loved. The mind, to be right, then creates experiences to prove that the assumption is true. Relationships often bring up old unresolved patterns from the past. Your old programming is running your relationship unless you take charge! Clear *your* own perpetrations first. Then, in a peaceful state go beyond your programming and explore the following options:

1.   Own your own reactions to people, not blame *them* for *your* feelings.
2.   Let go of premature judgment. Be in a peaceful place to make decisions.
3.   Have compassion for yourself and others, understanding that they (and you) did the best they could at the time.
4.   Kindly share your *feelings* and *wants*.
5.   Ask questions to clearly communicate that you want to understand.

Resolving Perpetrations to Renew Your Mind

Understanding your self-deceptions and releasing your subconscious fear-based programming RENEWS your mind. When you see what really happened (the truth), you can change your response and heal the perpetration. Since a perpetration is something that you believe to be so, that really isn't, or something that you think you should do that you don't, you are free to:

a. Explore where those feelings came from,
b. Own them (accept them as yours alone), and
c. Surrender to the truth.

You can stop blaming your environment, your mate, your co-workers, etc. for your problems. You can take responsibility for your life. How often do you "should" on yourself or another? Distortion and blame can happen without your realizing it!

The mind reacts to outward appearances, whereas spirit responds to inner reality. This is why decision making is far more successful when you are in a peaceful state. A perpetration is lurking behind every negative or moody attitude. Spirit in control brings a sense of peace and harmony, a knowing that all will be fine.

You can experiment with this "perpetration principle" and see for yourself. You can magnify a hidden part and go behind the surface content of your life to understand the underlying forces at work. You can have a wonderful time discovering for yourself how you, and others, are programmed.

You can trace your feelings to their source using Muscle Response Testing (MRT) and see how they are based upon false beliefs. Those false beliefs justify the perpetrations that lay hidden in one's mind.

We All Have Models for Loving That Affect Our Programming

Your mental capacity to give and receive love is affected by your first models of love, mother and father. If you believe they treated you poorly, you can develop an attitude that when you love someone, they treat you poorly. However, this is not to say that you were necessarily treated poorly, but to your mind, you were. Often a parent does not realize that their child is feeling ignored. They become preoccupied with "more important" affairs. Children rarely come out and openly complain about their life or share their feelings. They are more likely to fuss over something they do or do not want.

Many adults grew up with the adage that "children are to be seen and not heard." Therefore, it was common to conceal feelings, not knowing that these suppressed emotions could later develop into patterns of behavior affecting one's health and happiness. Of course, when positive feelings are experienced with early programming, the same is true. You are more likely to attract someone who treats you well, as your parents did.

For instance in the story, *Our First Demonstration of Love*, (*A New Day in Healing*, p. 135) Mary's father left her mother at a very young age. She never got to know him because he showed up only occasionally for brief encounters. Her first model of male love kept leaving her. In her heart she hurt for Daddy to be gone so much. Along with loving Daddy, she was always missing him and angry with him for not being there. Of course, talking about him was not OK for her, because Mommy was always mad at him. As she grew, loving a male attached to her feeling: "he's not there for me." Therefore, when she got to dating age, every time she had a male companion he would leave. She finally married, only to get a divorce. She was very discouraged in ever wanting to attempt another relationship.

Her mental programming was built upon a lie (self-deception). Mary believed that her father left because he didn't care about her, that something was wrong with her! Often children feel responsible when the parents do not get along or they feel inadequate in doing anything about it. Mary's perpetration caused her to be very uneasy around men and to distrust them. This programming set her up to attract unstable or insecure men who would leave. Her mind could then be RIGHT!

Mary had not created a successful intimate loving relationship up to that time. Her earlier experience caused her mind to be divided about having a successful male relationship. She *thought* she wanted to, but *felt* she didn't. **Her left brain logic and right brain feelings conflicted with each other** with her subconscious feelings winning out. Remember, subconscious feelings usually get their way, because they account for at least 80 percent of one's behavior.

In a Kalos Process, she realized that her dad really did love her and was very sorry to leave her behind. She got to see how her early childhood programming had controlled her life. She went on to resolve her distrust toward men and opened her heart toward her father. By healing her inner wounds, she is now in a happy fulfilling relationship.

You Experience Great Relief
When the Truth Is Known

Beliefs formed before learning to speak become locked into the body cells. People who have difficulty speaking their feelings usually have experienced deep emotional stress before the age of speech. All of this programming is accessible through The Kalos Process.

When faulty programming is exposed and released, great relief is experienced. A light, open feeling of gratitude comes in and fills the empty space left by the old lie.

Emotional backed addictions are no longer a mystery. It is easy to trace how, where and when the problem began. Often, patterns began in a previous generation. The pattern is passed down, just like the color of your hair or eyes. Emotional patterns that create detrimental behavior such as molestation, physical abuse, and deep-rooted fears may go back several generations.

The good news is that you can do something about it! You can take responsibility for your life and take advantage of the power of the Spirit to heal your life. You can overcome these patterns with a commitment to do so, and be healed!

Chronic problems and dysfunctional patterns can be resolved when you fully grasp and use the Kalos Process. Many come with a marital problem, physical pain or career difficulties and the same Process is used to find and resolve the cause.

You can look into your own mind, and the "like minds" of those who are close to you. Your family has many of the same mental/emotional patterns as yourself. It was probably no accident that you were born into that particular family with those particular patterns. Maybe, you actually chose that mother and father! What would be the benefit of that? When you see the benefit of your choices, you begin to break your pattern of being a victim.

Trapped Emotions Can Be Released

Through speaking out your suppressed emotions, you can free yourself enough to create the space for the truth to show up. You can identify perpetrations much easier as you express your hidden fears and feelings. In the Kalos Process we call this "Creating Space." Because suppressed feelings expand and turn into strong emotional subconscious reactions, they can cause either cellular activity (physical ailments) or unusual behavior (mental illness). Remember, any threat to your body results in a wake-up call of some sort.

Speaking out trapped emotions is not used to "make wrong" or blame anyone. They are of your making, not theirs. Therefore, they are for your healing, no one else's. You are the one to see "the truth" of the matter, eliminate the false judgment that caused them to be there, and set yourself free. You can take charge of your life by taking responsibility for it. This means owning your reactions to other people, knowing that they are there because of your programming, not theirs.

Your Mental Attitude Is Important for High Energy and Health

Your attitude determines the way you handle stress. You cannot control what happens to you, but you can control HOW you respond to it. This is why attitude is the greatest determining factor of your health. When you feel moody or discouraged, your energy level drops. Vital energy is needed to stay well and resistant to infection and disease. Your attitude has much to do about how you handle stress. The less will to live, the lower your energy level. The lower your energy level, the less will to live. This vicious cycle can cause a downward spiral to disease.

When in a great attitude (GRATITUDE), there is a zest for living and enthusiasm about your life. Living your special purpose lightens your life and nurtures a great attitude. There is a knowing that everything will be all right, even work a benefit for your life! Trust grows and faith moves you to accomplishing the purpose of your life. When your life has meaning, you seem to walk as on a moving sidewalk in airports, just flowing along. If you are struggling to live, not enjoying your career, your family, your relationship, your location, etc. you might end up in a "wake-up" call to bring you back on purpose with your life. This "wake-up" call is what we call dis-ease, because you are "out of ease" with your life. Lighten up! Life is too important to take it seriously!

Mental or Emotional Overload Can Cause Emotional Dyslexia

When you become overwhelmed with mental or emotional stress, the left and right hemispheres of your brain can "switch off." This overload causes the reaction of becoming super logical or super emotional, depending upon your basic nature. Neither mode, working alone, functions very well. For your mind to optimally function both hemispheres must function simultaneously. Details on dyslexia are found in *Chapter Nine* of this text.

Freedom from or Freedom to

We all have the ability to observe where we are *coming from* or *going to* in any given moment. Observing this aspect of mental functioning can bring more joy to your life. The question to ask yourself is, "Am I functioning out of needing to escape something (needing *freedom from*) or am I functioning out of choosing to. . . (the *freedom to*)?" Only you can know for sure.

The mind is never totally satisfied. Therefore, the mind is always seeking the *freedom from* something. The mind functioning from its needs, is always looking for something more, better or different to do, say, think, or feel. The natural functioning of the mind is to analyze, evaluate and compare. Yet, when it comes to enjoying your life, you cannot compare it to anyone or any situation because as soon as you do, you become engulfed in your judgment. The old judgmental mind can't win! When you are in any need, choice is hidden. The mind only wants to take care of the urgency and help you survive (discomfort). Appearances hide your *freedom to* CHOOSE! You always can find something to *run from* and you always have choice - to "choose to . . ." CHOICE functions in the present moment, through spirit, whereas the mind functions from its programmed needs. What is the conversation that goes on in your head when you are quiet? Does your mind think on the happy side of life? Do you take quiet moments to appreciate and applaud life or is your mind concerned about something? Notice when you are in choice and when you are "caught-up" with worry. You always have the freedom to think as you wish. You always have choice.

Living out of the viewpoint of *"freedom to"* gives you a powerful perspective to experience life from choice. The danger to the mind is that there is no one to blame, not even yourself! So "choice making" is not always comfortable. It requires having it OK to be "wrong," which means it's OK to be uncomfortable.

When you acknowledge your *"freedom to"* do something, your mind may become scared. If you don't resist the discomfort, just allow it to be there, you soon will experience peace and harmony. You enter the knowing that you are in charge of your life and that you are loving freedom more than fearing discomfort. A satisfying aroma of sweet essence fills your environment with a peace that cannot be described because it is unconditional, not dependent upon circumstances. You know that you can experience this anytime as you allow your mind to renew itself to trust.

When you imagine that you can create your world, it opens and releases new energy in your life, allowing you to be in charge. A new joy unfolds! A new gratitude expresses itself! A divine connection is realized, as you transform your life by allowing divine consciousness (spirit) to renew your mind. This allows a healing mode to begin! Understanding the mechanisms of your mind and the emotions trapped there will help you do The Kalos Process well and fulfill a happy life.

Laws govern every area of our lives, whether we are aware of them or not. As you become aware of the laws operating in your midst and take responsibility for your thoughts, feelings and actions, you will begin to see the harmony in the universe that brings healing and joy. To create full potential results in your life:

1. Own your own feelings and reactions to people.

2. Let go of premature judgment and come to a peaceful place before making decisions.
3. Have compassion for yourself and others.
4. Share your feelings and wants in a kind way.

The Highlights for this Chapter are replaced by reviewing the Mental Precepts.

The Mental Precepts

- The mind is a complete library of everything that has ever happened to us, called programming.

- The mind is programmed for survival to be:
  Safe and protected - physically
  Correct (right, proper, justified) - mentally
  Accepted - emotionally

- Your mind would rather be *right* than happy and be *safe* than successful.

- The mind works automatically; therefore, is a wonderful servant, but a terrible master.

- The mind is programming; therefore, can only function in the past (gone and cannot be changed) or what it believes about the future (an illusion).

- The mind **must** be RIGHT to survive.

- The mind functions in a way that before anyone can say or do anything, it must believe it is right, proper, or justified (in that moment).

- Your mind has three tormentors:
  Did I do the right thing?
  Am I doing the right thing?
  Will I do the right thing?

71

- A question that boggles the mind is: "What am I willing to experiment with?"

- The mind functions from the belief that the purpose of living is to be non-disturbed.

- The mind is never satisfied, always wanting more, better or different - creating a paradox with wanting everything to be the same to be comfortable.

- Your thoughts and feelings affect your health, such as guilt, which suppresses your immune system.

- You are not your programming. You are the one observing!

- Every time you don't feel love and peace, a perpetration is involved.

- Perpetrations (deceptions) form from the mind's mistaken judgments.

- When a decision is made with intense emotion attached, it creates a pattern from that time forth.

- The mind reacts to outward appearances, whereas spirit responds to inner reality.

- Subconscious programming is accessible through Muscle Response Testing.

- Your mental capacity to give and receive love is affected by your first models of love, usually Mom and Dad.

- Left brain logic and right brain emotions can conflict. You can *think* one way and *feel* another.

- Deep emotional programming that occurs before speech makes expressing your feelings difficult.

- Trapped emotion spoken out loud creates the space for *truth* to show up and for resolution to take place.

- Suppressed feelings expand and turn into strong emotional subconscious reactions that can cause cellular activity or unusual behavior.

- Your mental attitude is the greatest determining factor of your energy level and health.

- Mental or emotional overload can cause the "switching off" of the right and left hemispheres of the brain, causing emotional dyslexia.

- Your mind is always seeking the "freedom from," whereas in spirit you function out of the "freedom to."

- You transform your life by the renewing of your mind, using spiritual consciousness.

Participant's Page

1. Explain to someone you love WHO you are (in a way they can understand) that you are not your mind.

2. Share three of your deepest fears with someone with whom you want intimacy.

3. Create a question of aliveness for your personal life that can motivate you to explore new possibilities for living your full potential. What are you willing to experiment with?

Chapter Four

Spiritual Principles

The Roles of Love, Faith and Grace in the Healing Process

Once I awoke in the morning with a big sore lump in my throat. As I laid there contemplating my busy schedule, I surely did not want to deal with a sore throat! In frustration, I closed my eyes, imaged my throat and asked my throat why it was sore. A quick thought arose, saying: "You have trapped hurt and anger here from yesterday's upset." "Oh no," I thought, "I blew it again by not speaking out my feelings. When am I going to learn?"

I was glad to find the immediate cause of my pain though, so I could understand how to alleviate the symptom. Holding my hands over my forehead (to release emotions from a subconscious level, as described in *Chapter Eight*) and imaging the person involved, I spoke my feelings out; the very thing I didn't do the day before. I immediately felt relieved of the inner conflict. Then, I looked through my friend's eyes to feel her feelings. I realized that love was there, not the anger I had imagined.

I realizing the source of my problem was not from what my friend said, but it was my own emotional reaction to what she said. I needed to own and heal my preconceived judgment about what went on. I did not respond maturely by sharing my feelings and asking more questions. Sharing my feelings would have prevented any misunderstanding from occurring. I felt sorry for my immature behavior and mentally asked her forgiveness. I then asked God to forgive me too, and heal my hurting throat, knowing that I would share personally with my friend when I next saw her.

When I finished my prayer, my doubting mind began insisting that healing takes a long time. Therefore, by using a "word of faith," I commanded all the negative thoughts to leave, plus the soreness in my throat by saying:

> *"I bind you doubt, fear and inflammation and take you out and away from my body and send you out to be healed. And I sow in faith, forgiveness and complete healing."*

Going about my day, about two hours later I discovered my throat felt fine and was completely normal! Reports like this are common. *Your Faith Can Make You Whole!*

Physical means were not used to heal my throat, although physical changes did take place. It simply wasn't necessary here because the cause was emotional. Instead, I accessed the natural laws involved by the following steps to my Healing:

1. **I asked the ailing part** why it was sick and <u>listened</u> to it answer me. (Feelings of anger, hurt and frustration were lodged there.)

2. **I took responsibility** for my condition through owning the thoughts and feelings lodged there and *spoke them out* to the person involved.

3. **I placed myself in the other person's shoes** to understand why they acted that way and discovered they meant no harm. Realizing the truth *changed my attitude*. Knowing if I felt hurt or angry, it was because I was in a perpetration, I linked my reaction to an earlier time when I felt unloved.

4. **I compassionately forgave** myself for reacting and acknowledged that my friend had done nothing to require forgiving.

5. **I spoke a "word of faith"** (took authority) over my throat by commanding the inflammation to leave.

You may wonder from the preceding story, as I did many years ago, what really made the difference in my immediate healing. Was it because I understood the cause of the sore throat and released the trapped emotions, or was it a miracle from God, or both? Clearly, I did not take any pills or have any physical treatment to alleviate the symptom. I have come to believe *laws govern the healing process*. Repeatedly, I have seen the body restored to wholeness when the cause was identified and corrected, not mattering whether it was mental, emotional, or physical. I have also seen miracle healings when an accident occurred and nothing could be done about the cause; yet, by using the "word of authority," the grace of God intervened!

In the story of my throat's healing, all I needed was to get to the source, release the emotions involved, and speak a "word of faith." To speak a "word of faith" is simply to "take authority" over a problem through making a declaration that changes negative energy or imbalance to harmonize with health. Releasing spiritual love and forgiveness creates a change in one's blood and cells of the body. These actions created immediate results. Supernatural laws took effect as I asked the inflammation to leave my body. Every time one speaks, energy changes. I wish all could fully realize the power of one's **word**. Your words influence your world much more than you realize. Your WORD is as powerful as a two-edged sword, cutting positively or negatively.

Aligning with Spiritual Principles

Spiritual Principles — These are laws that go beyond physical understanding, yet affect our physical world and our aliveness; such as the law of giving, which creates abundance; the law of forgiveness, which creates healing; and the law of faith, which creates miracles to happen.

Principles of the spirit include the following attributes: Unconditional love, joy, kindness, understanding, faith, trust, forgiveness and patience. The mind must humbly surrender in order for these principles to be actualized in the physical world. By surrendering my mind's need to be right about how wrong "they" were, I could align to these natural spiritual laws that are always in operation. We can take advantage of the blessings they bring by surrendering our will to the will of the Spirit, rather than staying in the "reasons" of our mind. Someone once said,

"There are reasons and results, and reasons don't count."

Some Spiritually Fortifying Exercises:

1. Prayer and meditation (being silent, asking and listening, including letters to God–as explained in Book One, *A New Day in Healing*).
2. Speaking and proclaiming the word of faith (the substance hoped for, the evidence not yet seen).
3. Aligning to moral laws of love, kindness, patience, truth, integrity, fairness, and empowering others.
4. Being a vehicle for the Holy Spirit to express special gifts, such as: Gifts of healing, faith, knowledge, wisdom, miracles, tongues, etc. I Corinthians 12:27

Faith Is Always in Operation — Positive or Negative.

Maybe we all have faith.
It's just that some have faith in the negative.

Listen to the conversation that goes on in your head. Does it support your wellness and faith? Or are you weakening your body by the very words you say? When something happens that you do not like, do you say, "Oh, just like I expected, that's the story of my life." Your words are <u>powerful</u> and change energy immediately. <u>Whatever you say becomes validated at the energy level of existence</u>.

"O.K. but it probably won't work." - You're right.
"It will work, no matter what they say." - You're right.

If you think or say, "Oh, that person makes me sick," every time you see that person you will feel awful. You can actually create illness THROUGH YOUR SPOKEN WORD! You are powerful and your WORD is action, either positive or negative. Remember, your mind would rather be right than happy. I have seen people create problems in their lives by (negatively) proclaiming them into being, just through their words.

You are powerful and your WORD is action, either positive or negative. <u>So after you speak a word of faith, do not send it away by your doubts and fears</u>. Support your FAITH with ACTION. See balance, see healing, see results.

A Lady Whose Words Precipitated Her Disease

I remember a lovely lady who had cancer of the breast-bone. She had complained for years about her husband's smoking habits. She hated it and insisted that cancer would result if he didn't stop. She was frustrated and worried that the smoke would endanger her health. She also believed that smoking was breaking a spiritual law, according to her faith. The strange truth is that the cancer happened to her, not to him. A deep resentment and feeling of being unloved by him were found growing inside her body. Her belief was that if he really loved her, he would quit smoking. Feeling unloved, she wanted to die (subconsciously). Consciously, she wanted to get back at him for not listening to her. She became grossly deformed in her sternum, the very area that she thought attracted him the most (her chest). You can ask yourself if you have a hidden conversation going on inside that could grow into something too?

The Kalos Process was developed to help you go deep into the cause. Often the patterns of illness go back in time to when you were a child. I have seen rapid healing take place because of resolving a relationship with mother or father. Hurts from the past keep coming up in your life until the cause is corrected. Our body is like a barometer showing us what is happening on the inner plane.

Jesus said, "It is not what goes into the body, but what goes out of the body that defiles the man."

Defiling your body begins with your thoughts, and moves outward through words and deeds. Words are powerful and have a cutting edge to them. Words change energy immediately. Do your words support your wellness and the wellness of those around you?

The miracle that happened to me, mentioned earlier, can happen to anyone who wants the miracle of forgiveness and love. Aligning ourselves with love will pierce through the judgments of the mind and allow us to surpass the emotional and mental blocks to healing. I believe that as all are created in the image of God, all then can release the love of God from within. Maybe all the attributes of God are within us and wholeness is the REALITY!

Beliefs Can Affect Your Healing Process

One woman once said to me that she believed God wanted her to be sick so she could learn a lesson. I asked her what it was she needed to learn and if she had learned the lesson yet. She told me that she wasn't clear on what the lesson was and that it would take time. I suggested that maybe her lesson was to learn that God doesn't want anyone to be sick! She thought that to be a strange belief and therefore could not accept it. I told her that I would be happy to assist her after she learned whatever she believed she needed to learn and would then allow God to heal her. I knew that she would not be able to respond to any healing endeavor, as long as she believed that God wanted her to be sick. How can you trust a God that wants you to be sick or suffering? I am sure that God can create every experience to be a benefit, but how can you lower God's love to be less than your own? Would you want anyone to be sick? *"By your faith you are healed."*

You can believe in a remedy when it's only a placebo and still have it work about 30% of the time, yet doubt a highly successful procedure and nullify its effects. You can be healed miraculously, lose faith, then lose the healing. You can believe that you are the only one for which a Kalos Process won't work and you might get to be right.

Where is your FAITH? For those of you who are working in the healing arts, always work within a person's belief system and you will get results. Don't push or ever attempt to change a belief. There is always a way to expose "*the truth.*"

Faith, Trust and Surrender

Our body is made from the very substance of the earth. Should we not be in dominion over it? We, as spirit, utilize a body. We are not our body. We cannot be what we use. Is it possible that our body was created to serve our spiritual purpose? Moreover, could it be that we create out of intention? You can ask yourself, "What do I want to create? What is my intention for my life?" Look at the possibility that you are programmed in the following three ways:

- Your *body* wants to be comfortable;
- Your *mind* wants to be right and to be accepted;
- Your *spirit* wants to fulfill a meaningful life purpose.

Sometimes conflict lies between these three intentions. Which one is your motivator in life?

Within each of us is the power to take more control of our lives. Not by taking control through a struggle, but by taking control through surrendering and letting go to divine Spirit. Spirit never needs anything because spirit is full, sufficient and indestructible. Therefore, you can yield to the deeper truth behind any situation and see a benefit in it. There is always reason to give thanks. There is always a viewpoint that brings peace and understanding. Spirit is not afraid to look at another viewpoint. Spirit is not threatened by circumstances or situations. Faith is knowing that everything will turn out fine. When healing happens through the miracle of faith, we are sending out trust from the very center of our being to heal.

Preparing the soil for trust to flourish is more of a "letting go" than a grabbing hold of.

Choosing to trust does not usually feel comfortable, but can be exciting. Trusting is a way of saying, "I know that everything will be all right." There is no way that anyone can go back in time and prove that any part of your life would have been better had you made different choices. So since life is an ongoing event that is constantly changing, you can trust all will work for your highest good. Trusting cannot hurt you and you can have a wonderful time experimenting with it.

If you feel you are a slave to your appetites or desires, speaking the word of faith can set you free. Acknowledge your weakness and surrender to living according to the spirit, even if it's uncomfortable! If you have emotional problems, or any kind of problem, you can deliver yourself from it. God wants you to be well!

Is it Faith or Grace?

Faith comes from knowledge and is based upon beliefs. Grace means unmerited favor and shows up unexpectedly. Having no respect for one above another, grace is for all, deserved or not. I like what one person said of faith,

> *"Faith is not your ability to believe, but trusting God's ability to deliver."*

Sometimes a gift of faith appears and we immediately <u>know</u> or <u>sense</u> that we are healed. Often, Jesus said,

> "Your faith has made you whole."

The power to heal seems to come from the person being healed (their faith) rather than an outside source. While with grace, it is usually an instantaneous healing not expected. Grace and faith are as active today as two thousand years ago. God loves to work miracles through us and to us. Are we proclaiming results or enduring a negative faith? Words are powerful, choose them WELL.

<u>Miracles are natural laws that happen in the spiritual realm.</u>
They are called miracles because they supersede physical laws. They function on spiritual laws of cause and effect.

Maybe miracles are natural in the spiritual realm, though supernatural in the physical world. Getting our doubting mind out of the way may allow the natural to happen, more than making something spiritual to happen. *The more I trust and focus on my divine purpose, the more I notice miracles showing up in my life.* Understanding the workings of the spirit is to understand the laws of God.

Grace comes unexpectedly, unmerited from outside ourself. Faith is that which comes from inside and flows outward - our very essence inherent within us all.

Faith quiets our emotions. As we enjoy Faith-full thoughts, feelings of <u>appreciation fill our heart and fill our lives</u>. FAITH is nurtured with knowledge and experience, while GRACE shows up and we "know not from where it came." Whether healing comes from faith or grace, both bring rejoicing.

To see faith in action, you might want to attend a spiritual healing meeting, where people come for a miracle. There are training programs you can take on how you can express your gift as a healer. It was found systematically that a group of people can be trained to do spiritual healing and get a 40 percent success rate. That's a good result! Forty percent are great results for people who have simply learned to speak out a word of faith or knowledge. Problems can recur though, if the cause has not been checked. Often, when Jesus healed, he addressed *the cause* as sin (a broken law) by saying, "Thy sins are forgiven."

Often the cause goes back to not forgiving themselves or another. Therefore, with the cause not dealt with, about half of these people lose their healing by the time they get home. Another half has the old problem return within the following year. So TAKE CARE OF THE CAUSE TOO! In the following story you can see the steps to healing in action.

The Miracle in Finding the Cause

Once, when I was making rounds at a cancer clinic, I was asked to see a young man who was not making any progress. He had come from another clinic where the same unsuccessful attempts had been going on for three months. His condition was serious. This was his second episode with the same kind of cancer. I ended up doing a Kalos Process with him to understand why he unknowingly had opened the door to cancer. Deep resentment and guilt were hiding within the grapefruit size growth on his neck. We traced the cancer's beginning back to when he had been a missionary in Mexico and had severe problems getting along with a companion. Right there in The Kalos Process, he saw how anger and resentment toward his missionary partner had grown and become encapsulated by his body.

As he walked in his companion's shoes and looked through his companion's eyes, he saw the truth of why his friend acted the way he did. Seeing the situation from his companion's viewpoint transformed his negative feelings into compassion and love. By letting go of his preconceived judgment, there was no more need for the body to wall off his feelings.

This began an immediate healing process, which allowed him to be released from the clinic the following week - completely healed! I remember his excitement as he jumped out of the chair and ran to call his wife. "I am healed," he shouted, "I am healed!" Within the week, the large tumor released itself from his neck and the hole filled naturally. Finally, all of the natural methods of healing that were provided at the clinic without results took effect. Reviewing the steps to this man's healing:

1) He understood the cause through using a Kalos Process.
2) He actuated his faith by seeing the "truth" of the matter.
3) He aligned himself to spiritual principles and forgave his companion, then lovingly came back into communion with God.

Often the cause of the ailment goes back to buried resentments about oneself or another. When the cause is unveiled and forgiveness is achieved, a "healing mode" begins. A "healing mode" means that the body is doing all it can, as fast as it can, in that moment, to bring the body to wholeness.

A Razor Cut, Instantaneously Healed

The first time I witnessed an instantaneous miracle in action was when I caught my son playing with razor blades. He cut his finger severely and I was quite frightened. I grabbed his little hand and proclaimed, "In the name of Jesus Christ and by the authority of the Holy

Spirit, cut be healed!" The cut immediately disappeared and you couldn't even tell it had been there. If I hadn't seen the blood, I wouldn't have believed it myself.

This incidence was an act of grace, and spoken faith. Often I have seen the prayer of faith in action. When the gift of faith appears, you <u>know immediately</u> or <u>sense</u> that you are healed.

Often faith healings take place without a person understanding the CAUSE of the problem. When this happens, the problem will usually return in the same or a similar way. In the story of my son and the razor blades, removing the cause was easy. I simply needed to use much more care in keeping dangerous items from his reach — blades cut!

My Own Healing through Grace

As a child, my own family didn't go to church; therefore, I was taken by a neighbor lady, Mrs. Piper. I was drawn toward spiritual teachings at a young age. My mother died when I was nine. Through grief, my father began excessive drinking, making it difficult for me to connect.

As a result, I turned inside for my security and looked to Jesus for direction in my life. At the end of my twelfth year, I moved in with a wonderful foster family, Ann and Denver Duncan, who nurtured me and satisfied my craving to understand God. Often I felt comforted and nurtured by a caring God through my studies, prayers and meditations.

In my mid-twenties, a profound transformational experience happened that changed my attitude forever.

I was teaching a spiritual class for instructors at church. It was the fourth class in a series on some basic religious principles of faith, repentance, baptism and the gift of the Holy Spirit. Each time I taught, I fasted that day to prepare myself for spiritual guidance as I taught. This day was no different. My oldest son, Don, used to joke that the reason Mom was so thin was because she was always fasting. When I arrived home after this meeting, it was probably around ten o'clock at night. The four children were asleep and my husband was away that night. I was experiencing great appreciation to God for the class I felt privileged to teach. As I walked down the hall of my home, a light appeared around me. Then, I began feeling warm all over. This warmth became like a fire, as my whole body felt consumed. I experienced joy like never before. It felt as if every cell of my body, plus my spirit, was being purged and cleansed from every impurity. For the first time in my life, I felt completely clean. I felt pure and forgiven of every wrongdoing that I had ever done in the past. I felt like a new person.

This process went on for about two hours. In the midst of it, I experienced something unbelievably horrible, yet phenomenal. I saw a vision of my oldest daughter being raped and killed. I stood there experiencing love for both my daughter and the rapist, even though the act was abhorrent. While feeling this event to be the worst possible act to happen, something moved within my heart — all anger and judgment left. It felt as if I could not hate anyone anymore, even if I wanted to. It just was no longer in me to do it. The warmth stayed for many days. The love is staying forever.

The amazing result upon my body was that I no longer had cramps, pains or headaches. I stopped getting sick, as I usually did with sore throats or flu. I noticed that I had more energy and a clearer vision about my life. A difference in my health showed up from that time on. I knew the New Love had changed my life. Later, a friend labeled this as a "baptism of fire" experience. My healing was of the Spirit, and I knew it. This experience stayed with me, as I went into the healing arts. I wanted others to experience the same Love and Peace that surpassed understanding. I wanted everyone to be healed.

Ever since this experience, I have felt that the key to perfect health was of a spiritual nature. I do not separate Spirit from wellness. My proud and fearful mind, that tormented me with doubts and fears, was no longer in control. Instead, a submissive mind, supporting me to glorify God, took charge. My attitude changed completely. I saw Life as a wonderful gift and God as the giver.

Compassion filled the space where judgment had been. I stopped seeing love and peace as something to be learned or achieved. A holistic view replaced my narrow vision. I met a nonjudgmental God, who brought understanding to the term "unconditional love." I experienced how much God loves us all, no matter what we have done or how often we err. Fear was replaced by peace, confidence and assurance. My own healing brought me to wanting to serve God fully and teach others the way of Love. My struggle ended as I entered a peaceful way of exploring life, trusting and being filled with enthusiasm to see Life through a new viewpoint, through new eyes - the eyes of unconditional love.

I feel that every healing has a miraculous element in it.

The very nature of healing calls upon our faith and beliefs on conscious and subconscious levels about whether our body can heal or not. I have seen many miracles and thank God for the simplicity of spiritual healing.

FAITH and BELIEFS show up in your ATTITUDE and make the biggest difference in your health. The medical profession assures us that the vast majority of ailments stem from a nonphysical cause - "As a man thinks, so is he."

You Have Been Given Authority and Promised Dominion

Your word is powerful! Scripture tells us that "Our word is as powerful as a two-edged sword." I believe this, as I have seen healings take place by just speaking a word of authority over a problem and it disappears. Jesus promised us that we could do what He did, "and even greater..." This kind of healing is considered a faith or grace healing.

Be specific and SPEAK THE WORD that heals.

There are different ways to "speak the word." Many people speak healing, in the name of Jesus the Christ.

They claim His authority over a person, as I did with my young child with the cut finger. There is power in using the name of Christ. Jesus taught acceptance of His suffering, so we would not have to suffer. See I Peter 2:24. Others say because of their relationship of oneness with the indwelling Christ they do not need to say the name. Their Spirit speaking in alignment with Christ's Spirit actuates the same power by the same Spirit. These people just make declarations which work!

A declaration is different from an affirmation. An affirmation is usually affirming something is true that you doubt. Otherwise, you would not need to use an affirmation. Whereas, a declaration is telling something to happen, or declaring what you already know to be true. To declare something is to bring it into being immediately on an energy level. Your word changes energy. How you "speak the word" is up to you. You can be divinely directed. Ask and then "be still" and listen.

You Can Command Your Body into Balance

You can learn to exercise a **"Word of Authority"** and discover how powerful spirit is in you. You can change energy at command. If thought is energy, how much more powerful it is to speak those thoughts out into form and see what happens. Knowing that you can be a major participant in your healing process is empowering.

The subtle energy field of your body responds immediately to command. This can be demonstrated easily through MRT. Sometimes, I bind and take authority over pain, virus, inflammation, chemical poisoning, or any ailment, as in the story of the sore throat. I tell it to leave! Each person can command their body to serve them at an optimum level by directly speaking to a body part. Muscles will relax when told. I can feel negative emotions leave as I tell them to go.

Miracles are invoked by your word of faith, and also the grace of God. I love watching this wonderful level of healing in action. Each of us has been given dominion over our body. Speaking the WORD can change an electrical flow. We are truly blessed with gifts to clear viruses, command toxins to dissolve, direct bones to go back into place and take charge of our lives. This type of healing is very humbling, knowing you are tapping a power much bigger than yourself. All have faith to access. You can learn to exercise positive faith to be in greater charge of your life. I feel all are blessed with much more GRACE and FAITH than they ever realized. You are invited to live these spiritual principles and experiment with the initiation of **trust** and **humility**.

The first Section of this text lays the groundwork for the hands-on Sections to follow. The Physical Laws, Mental Precepts and Spiritual Principles will enlighten your mind and heart to understanding all possible CAUSES.

Highlights

- Your faith can make you whole! Faith is not your ability to believe, but trusting God's ability to deliver.

- Spiritual Principles are laws that go beyond physical understanding, yet affect our physical world and our aliveness, such as the law of giving which creates abundance.

- Every time you speak, energy changes. You can command your body into balance. Subtle energies of your body respond to command.

- You can bind and command a virus, inflammation, etc. to leave. Be specific when you "speak the word" of healing.

- Preparing the soil for trust to grow, is more about letting go than grabbing hold of something.

- Some spiritually fortifying exercises are:
  Prayer, meditation, speaking the word of faith, loving and supporting others, writing letters to God and being a vehicle for the Holy Spirit to express special gifts.

- The Holy Spirit can purge your body of unwanted problems, enter in and heal.

- Faith is always in operation - positively or negatively.

- Beliefs affect your healing process. Faith can heal.

- You have the power within you to take control of your life. Surrender, not force, is the key.

- You are programmed in the following three ways:
  1. Your body wants to be comfortable.
  2. Your mind wants to be right and to be accepted.
  3. Your spirit wants to fulfill a meaningful life purpose.

- If you feel you are a slave to your appetites or desires, speaking the word of faith can set you free.

- Faith comes from knowledge and is based upon beliefs. Grace means unmerited favor and shows up unexpectedly, whether deserved or not.

- Miracles are natural laws that happen in the spiritual realm. Steps in one man's healing:
  1. He understood the cause through a Kalos Process.
  2. He actuated his faith by seeing the truth.
  3. He aligned himself to spiritual principles, forgave his companion, then returned to God.

- Every healing has a miraculous element in it.

- You have been given authority and promised dominion. Speaking "a word" over an illness is powerful. You are invited to use these spiritual principles more often!

Participant's Page

1. Write or share a story from your youth (or later) that demonstrates a spiritual principle in action. Share your intimate feelings and experiences in an inspiring way.

2. Explore spiritual growth and intimacy with God.

Chapter Five

The Wheel of Health

Four Areas Affecting our Wellness

Wellness is our original, natural state of being. When we "miss the mark" by breaking the laws of health, laws that govern every aspect of our being, we get sick. When these Physical Laws, Mental Precepts and Spiritual Principles are not kept, some type of problem occurs. We are designed to be well and live a joyful balanced life. Sickness and limitation are outside the symbiotic harmony of life.

When seeking the cause, we are not looking for a way in which the body made a mistake. We are looking for the reason why the body had to make certain alterations to keep its natural balance. Could all laws be a result of balance? Or is all balance a result of a law?

Whichever way it is, the body is forever compensating for physical or emotional threats. As we move along, you will discover a law is always involved that was not known and/or followed. The Wheel of Health is a model that shows the four basic components of health:

1. Nutrition/cleanse
2. Exercise/rest
3. Environment
4. Attitude

All causes relate to the breaking of natural laws, whether physically, mentally or spiritually. Notice that the first three categories relate to the domain of physical laws; while only the fourth category, attitude, relates to the mind/spirit connection. Though "Attitude" is only one section of the wheel, it is the largest section; <u>for our attitude is the largest determining factor of our health</u>!

Understanding The Wheel of Health can give you a way to evaluate yourself and to look at what area you could focus on for optimum well-being. All four areas have a significant effect upon your health. Look at your lifestyle and determine where you could improve the most.

When tracing a problem to its cause, I find that over 75% of the time it originates with an emotional pattern or dysfunctional belief affecting one's attitude. The American Medical Association reports that 70% of all ailments stem from emotional stress, or more accurately — how stress is handled.

How you relate to stressful situations
depends upon your attitude!

Overall, the cause of all diseases is approximately 10% Nutrition, 10% Exercise and Rest, 10% Environment, and **70% Attitude**. Of course, there are exceptions to this rule. You can look at your life and decide. Many ailments are 100% emotionally based. Our attitude is by far the largest factor of our health. This is why I call this Transformational Healing. Without transforming your attitude you will only recreate old problems. Only through changing your thoughts and feelings, can you change your attitude.

The Wheel of Health

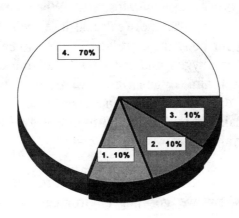

1. Nutrition   3. Environment
2. Exercise and Rest   4. Attitude

1. Nutrition

Nutrition may, overall, account for only about 10 percent of the reason for getting sick, but often plays an important role in regaining health. In some cases, like with blood sugar problems, the percentage is much higher. Foods can be remedies for many ailments, or they can be a critical factor in the cause of our problem. Food is fuel to replenish energy in our body. Too often the food we eat is denatured to the point of not having much energy left in it.

2. Exercise and Rest

"If we don't use it, we lose it!" When we do not use our muscles, they become weak and lose their tone. Exercise gives your body the circulation that is so badly needed to get proper oxygen and nutrients to all the cells, especially to the brain. When we starve any part of the body of oxygen, degeneration sets in. Rest, also, is a valuable factor in maintaining health and high energy. Resting the mind is as valuable as resting the body.

3. Environment - Water, Air, Radiation . . .

Everywhere we go, our environment is polluted to such a degree, it is imperative we keep our attitude positive and our immune system strong. You can do several things to protect yourself from a polluted environment. Use a water filter, to start. Avoid living in areas of polluted air, high power lines and noise pollution. People can pollute your environment with a bad attitude.

Examining all these areas in your life will help you see where you can improve. Are you doing all you can to support wellness for yourself and others? The remainder of this Section will address what affects your health the most, YOUR ATTITUDE!

4. Attitude

Your attitude is by far the biggest factor in your health, affecting how, why and when you: Get sick, get well and sustain profound well-being. It is your natural way of handling life situations and conditions from the deep recesses of your subconscious programming. Self-esteem greatly affects whether your attitude is positive or negative. Self-esteem shows how much you care for yourself. Until you can truly love and care for yourself, you cannot achieve much in caring and sharing your love with someone else. The second part of creating a perpetual positive attitude is the commitment to support others in loving themselves. The willingness to express love affects one's attitude more than any other factor.

Understanding the cause of a problem usually uncovers an emotional pattern that exposes one's attitude. Some people will get over one ailment, just to get something else. Their attitude brings them back to where they began.

<u>Our attitude is not dependent upon what others think, but what we believe about ourselves.</u> You can change your thoughts through understanding what the *truth* is about your life. You can experiment with the thought that whatever happens, a benefit is involved! The power is within you to choose anytime what you want to think. I decide whether I am living out of light (enlightenment) or out of darkness (the negative illusions of my life). My attitude is a barometer for me to see if I am in reality (what is so) about my life or caught in a self-deceptive illusion. I use the following statement as an **inner attitude check**:

Anytime I am feeling anything less than a peaceful, loving, harmonious state, I know that I am believing an illusion.

It is up to me to find the illusion and commit to the reality, which automatically changes my unwanted emotions and shifts my attitude back to peace again. Someone once said: "Our attitude determines our altitude."

When in a great attitude, I feel closer to God and my body functions in harmony and health. How I look at life's situations changes when I'm in a positive attitude. I can focus on what is going well or what appears wrong. Either focus has value, depending on the circumstances, and both have their consequences.

Attitude Is Formed in the Subconscious Mind

Attitude is the disposition of the mind, based upon emotions, subconscious tendencies and conscious orientation. When positive or negative feelings are <u>judged</u> by the mind (consciously or unconsciously) they turn into emotions! Emotion in Greek means "I-move" or "I-go," which means EGO! Emotions can be changed by changing your subconscious beliefs (judgments) and awareness. Emotions arise from the depths of the subconscious. Negative attitudes form because of subconscious beliefs made from fear-based programming that was not "seeing" clearly. As an example, when you hold a belief of: "<u>I am not good enough</u>," you then will:

- <u>Feel</u> not good enough, which is painful.
- <u>Compensate</u> by trying harder and harder to be good enough. An expression of this compensation could produce a "too good to be true" person, the compulsive pleaser.

- Depend upon what others say about you for your self-esteem, while needing constant praise to be "good enough." This can cause a vicious cycle of neediness and pretense, performing for seemingly unappreciative others.

Your attitude game thus has opposing beliefs — your story (what you hide and deny), i.e., "I'm not good enough" and your compensation (what you are trying to prove) "I am good enough." Even when you feel pretty good while in your compensation, there is no satisfaction in it, because you had to prove it! No matter how much praise you receive, it will never be enough anyway, because you don't really accept it. You can't win in this scenario. You only vacillate between feeling awful about not being good enough and feeling angry that you had to prove you were - a frustrating dilemma.

Another potential result of this no-win game is the inherent frustration that no one can ever really appreciate just how hard you try. No one understands! If you did encounter someone who appreciated and understood you, it still wouldn't resolve the game. You would continue to "act out" the unresolved dynamic until they left you in frustration of not being heard. Or you felt forced to leave them because you weren't heard.

Why aren't you appreciating yourself? Because you are still defending your deeply held secret: That you are not good enough! This is how "double mindedness" occurs, you *think* you are good enough and *feel* you aren't. (Later chapters will provide methods to test for and correct double mindedness.)

People who are operating from this kind of perpetration game usually attract others who do not express a lot of appreciation. This way they can REALLY BE RIGHT ABOUT THEIR GAME! Not receiving praise or appreciation can make one feel depressed or angry, but you <u>get to be right about not being good enough.</u> (If you were good enough, you would receive the appreciation that goes with being good enough.) Justification after justification then goes into play as you flip from depression to arrogance and anger, never really understanding why you are so upset so much of the time. Your core programming (your story) shows up constantly in how you perceive yourself and others.

Uncovering Your Prime Attitude Game

Pick up a pen right now and write down your biggest complaint about your life, your story. Stop, look inside yourself and find the part of you that is constantly bothered or not satisfied.

Example Stories:
I am not loved, appreciated, etc.
I am not good enough

Now, write down the first time you felt that way (your approximate age); what was going on, who was there, how did you feel? Write whatever comes to mind. Don't censor it, but allow your creativity to flow. Express all of your emotions fully. If you begin to feel emotional, hold your forehead over the frontal eminence bones while these thoughts go through your mind. (This will support you to release negativity from a subconscious level.) If you were too young to remember or nothing comes to mind, just start making it up and see what happens. You will find that you cannot make up what is not in your mind. Just experiment with it.

Notice what was going on when you made the decision that began this story about yourself. Notice how this decision came about. Look at how and why the other persons involved influenced this decision. Use **compassion** and you can probably gain understanding in any area at which you are truly willing to look. Love that little child that was doing the best he or she could. Look at the circumstances from your adult mind that understands why Mom or Dad acted that way, even if it seems like you are making excuses for them. The truth is they were doing the best they could under the circumstances. People act from the belief that they are right or justified in that moment, not knowing what is right, then doing wrong anyway, except with chemical addictions or compulsive behavior.

You can take responsibility for all of your negative behavior by looking at the stories you have made up about yourself and others. You have been the biggest perpetrator against yourself by believing: "There is something wrong with me!"

"Owning" Your <u>Prime</u> Attitude Game

Your game is the core agenda (your story) that goes with you always and under all circumstances.

Everyone has a prime attitude game. Everything you do is tainted with the energy of your core game. It is the underlying programming that affects all the areas of your life. When in an upset, it is there. Whenever you feel, "I knew it wouldn't work for me," or "I'm overwhelmed," the game is working well.

Since it is the basic program that runs your attitude, you do not want to resist it or deny it, only love and accept it. It is the bottom line programming that can be counted on to keep us safe. Billions of bits of information support this core programming.

You can make it fun and laugh watching your game, while appreciating the benefits it has brought you; or you can be hard on yourself. How you relate to your game is the very way you relate to other incidences in your life. Some say you can't change your game. Nevertheless, it can temporarily disappear by observing it and then choosing not to be driven by it in that moment.

My experience is that when you move from being a victim of your story to "owning it" and taking responsibility for it, in that moment, the game ends. You shine a light on the story so brightly that the deception within the story disappears. Don't resist it, embrace it and appreciate it. Through compensatory behavior, your game has brought you to being the capable person you are today.

Light is truth and the truth sets you free! The more you "own it," instead of being defensive or denying it, the less it comes up to be transformed. Count on the power of the Spirit to change this ingrained programming.

The Good News!

Because you have held negative beliefs about yourself, you have had to compensate for those beliefs. In fact, you have probably become extraordinary in some or all of the areas that you still feel inadequate. You see, the way the mind works is to pull you forward to achievement to be right, proper or justified. Your mind is always working for you to keep you SAFE and RIGHT!

So, though you still carry around that old story about yourself, it isn't even true! You just keep setting up your life to get agreement (collusion) that it is true. IT'S AN ILLUSION! Even if it were true once, and I doubt it, you have turned it into a strength!

A good example is a lady who came into our workshop wanting to get organized. She held a belief about herself that she simply was a disorganized person and therefore was always becoming overwhelmed with each task she had to do. She always felt behind. This created a constant negative response to life - never being caught up. She tormented herself with her own destructive thoughts (her story)!

When she looked at the REALITY (the truth of the matter) she discovered that because of her negative belief of not being organized, she had learned every way possible to become organized. In fact, upon questioning her I discovered that she had a reputation at her work at being the most organized person there!

You always have a CHOICE to look at the REALITY or to look at the ILLUSION. Your thoughts about your life determine whether you are committed to your story or the reality. Only you can promise to tell the truth.

Your thoughts are enlivening or destructive. You can choose to focus on that which is beautiful, supportive and of good report, or you can focus on negativity. It is up to you. You choose your own thoughts. When you have a negative commitment, stop and ask yourself what you are believing to be true that might not be true. Go back to a former time when you felt that way and look at what you were believing that turned out to be false. Since emotions are just judged thoughts, you can trace your thoughts and uncover the deception you are holding. Open to the possibility that it may or may not be true. You are in charge of the conversation that goes on inside your mind. Through The Kalos Process you can further learn a method to trace your mental patterns to their origin and clear up your deceptions.

Living Life Out of Truth and Out of Choice

First, heal the cause (perpetration) at the origin of your game. This will help you to tell the truth about yourself, that you are good enough. You will then feel good about yourself. Therefore, your attitude meets situations with a sense of value. You know that because you are good enough, you can do . . . and do . . . and do anything with a sense of knowing you've done your best. You prevent being driven to exhaustion to prove yourself through "over doing," thus adversely affecting your attitude, again. You also make allowances for yourself to "mess up" occasionally, after all, you're only human! When I am not feeling up to the task before me, I remember one of my favorite scriptures, "It is the weak things of the earth that I make strong." I simply turn my availability over to God's ability and surrender to do the best I can under the circumstances.

Living Your Full Potential Blesses Your Attitude

Knowing that you are living your life's purpose in your full potential raises your self-esteem and promotes a positive attitude. A positive attitude does not require regular reaffirming, such as positive thinking, but allows you to experience internal joy. A positive attitude becomes your natural way of being. What I am saying is that you can BE the space of a perpetual positive attitude. You can live a joyous life by living in integrity to the dream within your heart, your passion! You can develop the positive attitude habit once you acknowledge who you are (tell the truth!), proclaim your life purpose, and live it! Joy is the result! Ask yourself: "How do I want to express my full potential of love and caring in the world?" Read *Chapter Five*, *A New Day in Healing* for further commentaries on attitude.

The Kalos Process has a lasting effect upon your attitude. As your attitude changes, your mind renews. As your mind renews, your life transforms!

Now that you are equipped to understand the possible causes, the next Sections invite you to practice the techniques to GET TO THE SPECIFIC CAUSE!

Highlights

- The body makes alterations to keep itself in balance. Could all laws be a result of balance? Or, is all balance a result of a law?

- The body compensates for physical or emotional threats to preserve our lives.

- You will greatly improve your health by understanding and aligning yourself according to the Wheel of Health. The four areas of wellness are:

  1. Nutrition
  2. Exercise and Rest
  3. Environment
  4. Attitude

- How you relate to stressful situations depends upon your attitude.

- Though nutrition may not be the underlying cause of your problem, it may play a valuable role in regaining health.

- "If you don't use it, you lose it!" Start an exercise program today!

- Environmental illness has become a major threat, causing more people to live limited lives away from pollutants.

- Our attitude is by far the biggest determining factor of our health. It is the part of us that automatically reacts to any situation or circumstance.

- Our attitude is our natural way of handling situations and conditions from the deep recesses of the subconscious mind.

- Our attitude is not dependent upon what others think, but what we think about ourselves.

- You have the power to change your attitude. To transform your attitude is to transform your life.

- Your Prime Attitude Game is your core agenda (your story) that goes with you always and under all circumstances.

- When you move from being a victim of your story to "owning it" (taking responsibility for it), in that moment, the game ends.

- You are either committed to the REALITY (truth) or the ILLUSION (your story). You can tell by how you feel in any given moment.

- Through the Kalos Process you can trace your mental patterns to their origin and clear up your deception.

- You can live a joyous life by living in integrity to the dream within your heart, your passion!

Participant's Page

1. For the next 24 hours, stay in gratitude - a great attitude! Think of everything for which you are grateful. Only give prayers of gratitude, ask for nothing.

2. Share your gratitude with someone else through a thoughtful word or gift that is not expected.

SECTION II

UNCOVERING THE CAUSE?

Learning Techniques to *Uncover the Cause* Using Muscle Response Testing (MRT)

One is either committed to the drama of forever healing, or one is committed to Be Healed – Reasons or Results?

Chapter Six

Your Bio-Computer

The Greatest Scientific Breakthrough

Can you imagine the excitement, in fact the whole world's excitement, if you discovered the most incredible bio-computer for analyzing human illnesses and behavior? What if you could easily print out an entire history of everything that had happened to you from within the womb to present time? What if this bio-computer could not only identify your subconscious beliefs, but also could tell you how that attitude began? What if it could easily tell you your lifelong nutritional patterns, as well?

What if your bio-computer could tell you when a specific fear started and when a biological problem began? What if it understood why you did certain things past and present, who was involved and what needs to be resolved to balance your life? What if it could tell you what was happening at the beginning of a problem, so that you could avoid illness, as well?

Well you guessed it! You not only have one, <u>you have a lifetime lease on it</u>! God has created our bodies to take in, store, and recover information as needed for our benefit. We are just beginning to appreciate the wonderful mechanisms of our physical form. Through your own body's electrical system, using Muscle Response Testing, you can now take charge of your life in an amazing way. What is even more astounding is that your bio-computer can recommend the type of healing modalities it wants and the specific sequence of priorities it needs for the most rapid healing!

The Most Sophisticated Bio-Electrical Machine on the Planet!

Our magnificent human body is much more than what meets the eye. It is a marvelous machine, each unique, yet with similar standardized systems. Each one is lovingly handcrafted with the same components, yet individually expressing itself.

Our amazing body is not only capable of building and repairing cells, but even reproducing itself. Every body is a complete bio-electrical, chemical plant that can manufacture everything it needs to stay alive. Even most minerals and all our vitamins can be produced in our body's bio-electrical plant.

The Synergistic Functioning of Our Body

Though the body has many incredibly designed components and systems, it is its synergistic functioning that creates the miracle. The whole is equal to much more than its parts. Parts of the body assist each other in a miraculous way. If one organ of the body needs extra energy, the other organs give generously what they can. One part of the body never stands alone. There is an integration of systems and supports to serve us.

Your body doesn't lie! You can trust it to tell you what you need to know to keep well and happy. It has the most complete communication system ever devised. Within your own reach is the most magnificent human machine ever imagined. The question is: Are you willing to listen to what it has to say? In this Section you will begin learning some simple Kalos methods to retrieve information on a cellular level to align yourself to the laws of health.

How Our Body Functions As a Bio-Computer

Our *bio-electric computer* is a highly sophisticated integrated machine-like apparatus. The following description isolates and distinguishes the various complex functions:

OUR BODY — Comparable to the "hardware" of a computer, is a symbiotic system of integrated parts made of tissues, cells, organs, etc.; coordinated by a Nervous System.

OUR NERVOUS SYSTEM — The sensing and communication system for integrating all the operations. The input through the sensory system and output through the motor nerves affect the muscles, organs, glands, etc.

OUR BRAIN — The Central Processing Unit controlling operations runs our complex body automatically through the electrical system, nervous system and endocrine system. Right and left brain function includes the storing of information through thoughts and feelings. This is why you can think one way and feel another. The memory bank of the mind, especially survival programming, affects brain function,

OUR MIND — Programming, like the "soft ware" of a computer, is the stored information that feeds back to the brain. Mental programming guards the body's survival, retains past experiences and runs automatically. Our mental filing system stores, retains and recovers information on conscious and subconscious levels to not only enhance our lives, but also to keep us alive as conscious beings.

Conscious thoughts become a part of our conscious mind programming. As soon as a thought happens, it becomes a holodyne (picture) in the mind. The Mind does not know the difference between the "thought" and the actual happening. It is all holodynes. Feelings are a result of thoughts and sense perception. Feelings cluster together and unknowingly control our attitude and subconscious programming. The Mind is programmed for survival. And the only way the mind can survive is for it to be RIGHT! Therefore, your mind is always working for you, to protect you from any embarrassment or from any discomfort you might encounter.

OUR ELECTRICAL SYSTEM — A network of energies in the form of Energy Centers (Chakras), Acupuncture Meridians and the Electromagnetic Field that communicates with the brain, via the Central Nervous System.

Our Electrical System connects our entire body structure together through the muscles; connects our organs through the meridians; supports our nervous system through neuro-vascular and neuro-lymphatic energy flows, uniting our spirit, mind and body into ONE.

Because of our intricate electro-chemical body, we can uncover information stored at a cellular level through a Muscle Response Test (MRT). All the muscles of the body connect to the brain by way of the nerves, electrical system and acupuncture meridians. Therefore, any information that is stored by the brain, tissues or cells is accessible through MRT. This is phenomenal! We are only limited by our knowledge of how and what to ask. We will go into greater detail on MRT in the next Chapter.

You are the Programmer of this wonderful bio-electrical organism! You can discover what is not working and what to change. You have dominion over your bio-computer. Therefore, the more you understand it, the more you can be responsible for your well-being.

Acupuncture Meridians Flow through Our Human Body

For more than 4,000 years, acupuncture has been used to <u>diagnose</u> and <u>prevent</u> illness. In fact, acupuncturists received pay to keep people well and avoid illness. If their patient did get sick, they were treated free of charge. Acupuncturists proved their worth by being able to communicate with and to balance a person's electrical body. They knew that before a body became sick, the electrical field would go out of balance. Their function was to keep the electrical body, through the acupuncture meridian's early warning system, in perfect balance.

Just as the blood vessels carry the blood through the body, the acupuncture meridians carry energy. It was discovered that these vessels of energy connect the muscles to each of the organs of the body. If, for example, the kidneys became weak, the level of energy to the upper trapezius muscles at the back of the neck could be affected. Or, if the upper trapezius muscles became tense, the level of energy to the kidneys could be affected. Our body is so interconnected that when any part is not functioning properly, the rest of the body can be affected.

The acupuncturists determined that the overly energized meridians were the inflamed areas in the body, possibly showing disease. As an example, when an organ or muscle had a problem and needed more energy to function properly, energy would build up to support the needy area. Acupuncturists knew exactly where to go on the meridian to unblock the energy and balance the system. They would then treat the needy area with herbs and foods to bring it to normal function.

In a demonstration to prove the powerful presence of the electrical body, Chinese scientists attached wires to a person's body in a special way. They showed how a person's own electrical energy could light a small light bulb!

Our Electromagnetic Field
Discloses Information

During the nineteen forties, Harold Burr at Yale University studied the energy fields around plants and animals. He found that we all have an electrical field that is aligned with the brain and spinal cord. Much to everyone's surprise, he discovered that this electrical field was that of an adult! He disclosed that an electrical blueprint of the body was already present at the time of the earliest development, even at the stage of an egg. Burr's data suggested that any developing organism was destined to follow a prescribed growth template and that such a template was generated by the organism's individual electromagnetic field. Further research has born out Burr's findings.[14]

Semoyon Kirlian, a Russian scientist, demonstrated that we have an electromagnetic field extending from our bodies through the use of electrographic recording techniques. Electrophotography is based upon observations of a phenomenon known as the corona discharge. Dr. Kirlian, for whom the Kirlian photography process was named, could detect disease in the body's electrical field. Through special photos, he showed diseased areas as dark spots in the energy field that extended beyond the physical body. Some call this field an aura.[15]

---

[14] *Vibrational Medicine*, Richard Gerber, M.D., 1988, Bear & Co.
[15] See glossary.

Burr and Kirlian found that diseases like cancer caused significant changes in the electromagnetic fields of living organisms. Burr revealed this by studying superficial skin measurements taken with his voltmeter. Kirlian recorded corona discharge images of the body to confirm the disease-associated energy field changes.

Kirlian photography showed that when a person was missing a limb, the electrical body still protruded out from where the limb used to be. This possibly explains why people who have had a limb removed continue to feel it there. All life, even inanimate objects, emit this auric field.

Communication at the Cellular Level

By communicating with your bio-electrical body, you can be aware of what is going on inside at a cellular level. This has two major benefits:

1)   You can prevent disease before it reaches a threatening level.
2)   You can uncover the cause of your problem and determine what is needed for healing.

Your body doesn't lie and wants to support your health. Your body has all the information needed to support you to get well and stay well. Being able to test your electrical body allows you to take charge of your health and well-being in a very useful and dynamic way.

Muscle Response Testing (MRT)

Muscle Response Testing connects us to all parts of the body through electrical impulses that travel from the muscle being tested to the brain. A magnificent communication system functions within the electrical body that can let us know what is going on at any time. All of the information stored in our body is available for our accessing.
The electrical body is the first sensing device of the body to pick up information for the body's survival. Problems show up in the electrical system before they appear in physical form, which can give us information in advance of any onset of illness. Just as physical symptoms show up before any illness, so does the electrical body show imbalances in areas that are the next to be affected in the physical realm. This is what especially makes MRT so valuable. We can know what is going on far in advance of any onset, making MRT a wonderful tool for prevention. We can stay well!

A complete description of MRT is in the following Chapter. They are vital components of the methodologies to resolving the cause of a problem. I recommend that you practice with someone knowledgeable in this area and be tested before going off on your own. You will be amazed at how quickly you can learn this art. "The truth is simple" has a familiar ring, and now accessing "the truth" can be simple also!

Highlights

- Our bio-electric computer is a highly sophisticated integrated machine-like apparatus.

- Through testing your own body, you can now take charge of your life in an amazing way.

- Our bodies have all the information that has ever happened to us contained within its cells. You can access that information through the use of MRT.

- Through your electrical body, you can uncover the cause of your problem and what is needed for healing.

- Muscle Response Testing connects us to all parts of the body through electrical impulses that travel from the muscle being tested to the brain.

- MRT discloses problems even before they arise in the physical realm, making it a wonderful tool for prevention.

Participant's Page

HAVE A DISCUSSION WITH A FRIEND ON THE FOLLOWING ISSUES:

1. What is the difference between your brain and your mind?

2. How do acupuncture meridians affect your health? How do they get blocked?

3. How can you treat your body with more respect?

Chapter Seven

How to Access Your Bio-Computer through Muscle Response Testing

MRT Can Read the Body/Mind

Muscle Response Testing (MRT) has created a revolution in the art of healing and is the most dynamic breakthrough in understanding our human body in this Century. To me, MRT is the most profound tool for communicating with the cellular level of the body in a non-invasive way.

Many patients have told me that what I revealed to them using MRT was exactly what they got from their medical tests; only my testing cost a whole lot less. MRT is meant to augment medical testing, not replace it. One advantage is that it can pinpoint the source of a problem that is causing medical uncertainty. Often a patient will be told that the medical test did not reveal exactly where the problem was located: "It could be your liver or your gall bladder."

Problems reveal themselves in the electrical system of the body first, before they appear in physical form. So, MRT can support you to uncover problems in the earliest possible stage, before any medical monitor could pick it up. Patients have come back because they know that MRT gives them more information than they had after spending hundreds or thousands of dollars on medical tests. Just imagine, when you have mastered the art of MRT, you too can trace a problem back to its cause!

Muscle Response Testing is a simple, workable gauge that gives a reading on the inner functioning of your mind and body. Because of the interrelationship between the muscles, organs, brain, nerves and electrical system of the body, you can uncover information held on a subconscious level. MRT is an accurate and revealing procedure that you personally can put into practice with a very little amount of training.

Trigger Point Testing Reveals the Answers

In the last forty years, several people, including myself, have contributed to developing and identifying "Trigger Points" on the body. The first points that I learned came from Dr. Riddler, a dedicated chiropractor in the Northwest. John Barton's valuable research gave us the Emotional Trigger Points.

Trigger Points are places on the body that are touched while using Muscle Response Testing to show whether the body is in balance - emotionally, nutritionally, chemically, and electrically. Through the electrical system, you can communicate with a specific part of your body at a deep cellular level.

Through these Trigger Points you can determine vitamin and mineral deficiencies, digestion problems, allergies, and imbalances in hormones, organs and blood sugar levels, etc. Your electrical body will indicate each part and system that needs balancing. The information about testing other Trigger Points, relating to physical conditions, is found in *Transformational Healing Series, Book Three, The Manual*.

Your body holds all the answers and all the data needed to understand your problems. How you deal with stress greatly affects your physical condition. You will find unresolved emotions hiding at the core of most chronic illnesses. You can detect what emotional stress is trapped in your body and where it is.

Testing Emotions through the Electrical System

The electrical body gives you all the information to decide what emotion is affecting what part of your body. This is a great breakthrough in healing problems that are particularly of unknown cause.

You can determine what emotions are blocked in your body, and reveal what circumstances in life brought them about. You can even learn what emotions are blocking the healing process itself. You can identify: when the problem began, what was going on, who was involved and what the body needs to heal! How to test the "Emotional Trigger

Points" is detailed in *Chapter Eight*. First, you will want to learn how to use Muscle Response Testing.

Preparing for Muscle Response Testing

The following is a description of how to accomplish Muscle Response Testing successfully. You can explore these techniques on your own. This text is not to replace hands-on, supervised practice. Please get some hands-on training from someone certified in this work.

1. Remove all potential interferences to test the body's subtle electrical energy accurately: jewelry, crystals, metal bands, all watches and plastic rimmed glasses. Gold and silver worn at the same time can cause a short circuit of your electrical system, as do batteries. Crystals may interfere by causing each test to test strong. Eventually you can test to see if any of these objects is interfering with the test.

2. Do not stand under fluorescent lighting, or by any other source of electromagnetic radiation, such as a running microwave oven or television screen.

3. Balance the three major electrical circuits by rubbing the following three areas of your body. This will align the energy flowing:
     a. Side to side
     b. Up and down
     c. Front to back

Circuit balancing ensures that the electrical communication between the brain, nerves and muscles works well for accurate testing.

A. Rub the clavicle bones at the base of your neck with your dominant hand, while your other hand is held over your navel to balance the energy moving from side to side in your body. Roll your eyes in the direction of a lazy figure 8 while rubbing. Notice that the flow goes up in the middle and down on the outside.

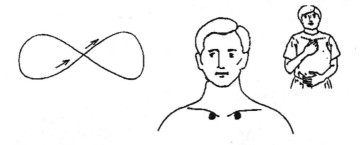

B. Rub above and below your lips with your dominant hand, while your other hand is held over your naval to balance the energy moving up and down in your body.

135

Roll your eyes in the direction of a vertical lazy 8 while rubbing.

C. Rub over the end of your tail bone with your dominant hand, with other hand over your navel to balance the energy moving from front to back in your body. Roll your eyes in the direction of a flat horizontal lazy 8 with you standing in the middle. Begin at your navel and move your eyes to your front left side, then around to the back like butterfly wings. Bring your eyes through the middle of your body out the front right side and repeat the movement bi-laterally.

With these three Electrical Circuits in balance, you are ready to begin Muscle Response Testing.

Doing Muscle Response Testing

1. **Stand to the side of the person being tested,** never directly in front of them, as your electrical field might interfere with their electrical field. Do not put your body too close to theirs or have your foot touching theirs, for you may end up testing your energy field, not theirs. Use your dominant hand to test. If you are right-handed, you will be standing on their left side and testing their left arm.

A Muscle Response Testing Stance

2. **Create a neutral testing environment** and look straight ahead. Colors and objects that have a special meaning, like a cross, can affect the test. Make sure your partner does not close their eyes during the testing, turn to look at you, or drop their eyes to the floor. Wear neutral colors, if possible. You are simply reducing interferences, while learning to test accurately. Eventually, your skill and focused intention will override interferences.

3. Have the person place their arm out from their side, parallel to the floor, then lower the tip of the arm about one foot for easier testing. Have them lock their elbow. Generally a shoulder muscle, the deltoid, is used for convenience. Any muscle will respond in the same manner. Never use an injured muscle or one in pain.

4. SLOWLY apply 6 to 8 pounds of pressure on their outstretched arm using one or two fingers between the wrist and elbow. Practicing with a scale will be valuable to apply consistent pressure. Give them a chance to keep their muscle locked in solid. Having them say "push" as they resist keeps them from holding their breath (which makes their arm too rigid) and allows an easier test. Begin pushing very slowly to give them a better chance to resist. Use only the pressure in your fingers. Do not get into a tug-of-war. There is nothing to prove. Never look to prove anything. You are simply allowing their body to release information from a subconscious level.

The person being tested should float their arm in a way that does not resist the pressure, yet holds and maintains consistency. In a strong test the arm doesn't move. In a weak test the arm moves downward. The test is determined in the first two inches of the arm position. Sometimes a person's arm only moves a small amount; other times it seems to collapse. A strong test should have a locked-in feeling like a brick wall. A weak test feels like a wishy-washy resistance, similar to a wooden fence. If their arm is very weak, you can apply pressure closer to the elbow, (not above it) to reduce your pressure.

5. Practice a strong and weak test. Work as a team while practicing MRT and do not try to prove anything through your testing. Your mind can interfere, so be neutral; don't be attached to the result by looking for a specific answer. *Focus on WHAT you are testing, not on a person's muscle.* Trust your fingers to tell you if a muscle is weak or strong; you just notice the response.

Practice a few times to be able to tell the difference between their strong and weak test, as every person's resistance is different. The following are some ways to find out what their strong and weak tests are.

A. While testing a person's arm, have them state their correct name: *"My name is Joan."* This should test strong. Then have them state their name as something else: *"My name is Jack."* This should test weak. If it doesn't test weak when they say an untruth, you are not applying enough pressure for their muscle strength. If both tests are weak, it means that you are pressing too hard or too fast.

B. Push down on your partner's arm to determine a strong test. Then have them think of a *negative emotion* such as anger, resentment or grief. Now push on their arm again and see how weak their muscle becomes just thinking of a negative emotion.

C. Using a *homolateral stance* can tell if you are able to determine a WEAK TEST easily — Your partner places their right leg and right arm out, balancing their weight between both feet, then test. This homolateral position should always test weak, because standing this way is awkward for the body. If by chance the homolateral stance tests strong, rub the three circuits again. Practice back and forth from a homolateral stance to normal until you get the feel of the person's strength, which is your gauge for getting an accurate muscle test.

Attitude for Appropriate Testing

- **Be in rapport with person being tested and treat the body with respect**

The person being tested is to take responsibility for the testing. Get feedback from them, because they may feel that you are pushing harder when the test is weak. This is common because their muscle does become weak; therefore, they have a difficult time holding it up. Let them be responsible for the test.

Repeat the test when necessary to be certain of the difference between a weak and strong test. You both need to know what a strong and a weak test feels like. Don't argue over any test. Repeat until both are satisfied or, if still not sure, consider the test weak.

• Tester must remain neutral and not use MRT to prove anything

Keep an attitude of: "I really want to know the truth." Your mind can interfere with the testing if you have preconceived ideas about what you are testing, or if it really matters to you how the test turns out. Without being honest and clear on your intention to understand "what's so," you cannot test accurately. Muscle Response Testing is a wonderful tool to use in helping you to be very honest and develop more integrity. I changed some prejudices against certain pharmaceuticals, as I tested and discovered some people needing them.

Your intention is most important. Focus on what you want to know and proceed. A humble, willing and focused tester will overcome interferences. Stay neutral and in integrity.

Do not use MRT to prove anything, as you can prove almost anything by interfering with the test. The test is very much affected by your belief system. If you strongly believe that potatoes are bad for you, they will probably test that way. If you are confused or looking for a specific answer, either you or your partner can interfere with the testing.

- ## A person you are testing is to remain neutral

Once I was testing a patient who looked exceptionally peaceful and happy. She stood there smiling with her arm out and not a single "weak test" showed up during the MRT. I knew this couldn't be possible because she had a lot of problems, but I couldn't find any of them. We just kept testing and testing until finally I said, "What are you thinking of?" (I thought she might be interfering with the test). She answered, "LOVE." I abruptly replied, "Stop that, you are interfering with the testing!" We both laughed and I had her look at the wall. It's best to keep your eyes open, mind neutral and look straight ahead when you are being tested, as thoughts can interfere.

- ## Never use MRT to make decisions for you

MRT is limited to what information has been stored in the memory banks of your body. You are the one to decide, not past programming. Never allow MRT to replace common sense. Be knowledgeable enough about what is "normal" to question, if the testing seems strange. Use it to the extent that you feel it is reliable and not when you are unsure. MRT is an art. The more you use it the better you become at it.

Hints on Accurate Testing

If your body or mental programming has the same problem as the person you are testing, you may have a difficult time in testing them. The two *same negatives* can cancel each other. For example, if you are working with someone with the same weakness as yourself, such as you both have a blood sugar imbalance or both have emotional frustration, the test may show up strong. Heal your issues first, so you can test someone else accurately. Everyone using MRT professionally is challenged to make sure they are in balance before testing someone else.

Sometimes your body may not want to uncover the *truth* about something because its comfort zone is threatened. Therefore, if you suspect this, make the following statement and test: *"The body wants to tell the truth."* If weak, ask the body to tell the truth and it will usually respond when it realizes it has been caught.

If the *water level* in the body being tested is very low, it can interfere with the electrical communication system in the body. Therefore, lightly pull the ends of a pinch full of hair in a flipping motion and test the muscle to check this. A weak test will require that person drink about a half cup of water before continuing.

Always do a strong test following a weak test. This gives the muscle a chance to recuperate and get its strength back before going to the next test. If the muscle stays weak, recheck to see if the question tripped thoughts or emotions, causing a circuit to go out. Recheck the circuits and correct if necessary.

It can be easy! Please do not get distressed over all the possibilities that can interfere with accurate testing. I want you to have a sense of how easy it is before being too concerned about interferences and mastering the technique. Just keep your mind focused on what you are testing.

Take the opportunity to practice MRT with a skilled Kalos Health Facilitator or Kinesiologist. Many types of health practitioners are using this work. You will be amazed at what you can do in a very short time. In this text we are introducing MRT as a tool to read information from your body, as relating to issues of an emotional nature. In the next book of this series, details on how to test your body for organ imbalances and vitamin and mineral deficiencies will be covered. You will learn how to do a complete wholistic physical examination!

Because your mind, even your subconscious mind can affect the test, it is a good idea to fill your mind with as much information about health as you possibly can. Read everything you can get your hands on. There are lots of marvelous books in print that will help you become informed on how the body and mind work. Be open to new information. Dr. Bernard Jensen used to say:

"When you're green you're grow'in.
When you're ripe, you're rotten!"

Staying humble truly opens you to testing clearly. Some have tried to prove that MRT doesn't work. You cannot prove anything with muscle testing (not even that it doesn't work), because it is too vulnerable and susceptible to influences. Use it as a tool, not a master and you will have success. MRT gives you the joy of individual responsibility and freedom. You can learn an efficient, yet harmless, way of knowing and caring for yourself in a meaningful way.

Practice - Practice - Practice

I encourage you to practice as much as possible at first to get a feel for the testing. Use it and grow by it. Use every opportunity to practice, even though you step outside your comfort zone. Practice on your family and friends. Find a partner that you can practice with every week for a few weeks. Practicing in a group allows you to test different people with different arm strengths. Some people are very easy to test while others are more resistant. The ideal situation is where two people work together to assist each other in getting correct information.

Muscle Response Testing will help you in developing sensitivity to your body. After testing becomes easy, you will find that you will intuitively pick up information from the body. You will be able simply to pick up a food and know whether it is good for you or not. That ability will give you an even greater sense of being in charge of your life. After supporting your own wellness, you will then be the space for supporting others to take responsibility for their health.

Surrogate Testing

Surrogate testing makes it possible for you to test small babies, invalids, and yourself. You simply test a person who is holding or touching another person or baby, who cannot be tested directly. The surrogate's energy

145

field will reflect the person they touch. Just as an electrical fence will shock the person at the far end of the line of people, so will the energy go to the end of the line, using MRT. In fact, you could make a long line of people holding hands, then test the person at one end and the person at the other end would be the one tested.

I recommend that you become familiar with using MRT on each other before using surrogate testing on yourself. However, I do recommend that you test yourself as soon as possible, so that you will benefit from the experience of taking more responsibility for your health and well-being. The more you practice the easier it becomes.

Testing Yourself

To test yourself, stand facing your partner, off to one side as pictured below. If you are right-handed, point the big toe of your left foot to the big toe of their left foot and slightly touch, leaving your right arm opposite their left arm to use in the testing. By connecting your body in this fashion whatever you are testing, though using their arm, is actually testing your energy field. Practice this a few times connecting and then disconnecting to see the difference in the test.

Testing Yourself

You will love this wonderful method for testing infants and even animals that can't tell you what is wrong or what hurts. You can expose the hidden cause of their problem.

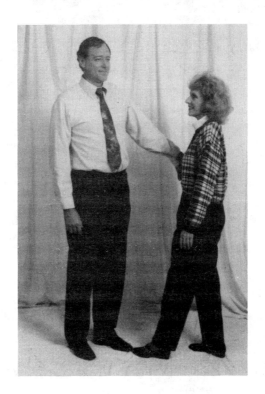

Highlights

- MRT has created a revolution in the art of healing and is the most outstanding tool, so far, where you can communicate with the cellular level of the body in a non-invasive way.

- Your body holds all the answers! In the last forty years, several people, including myself, have contributed to developing and identifying "Trigger Points" on the body.

- A Trigger Point is a place on the body you touch while using Muscle Response Testing that gives you a reading on whether the body is in electrical balance.

- Trapped emotions are identified through the use of MRT. Your physical condition is greatly affected by how you deal with stress.

- MRT is a simple, workable gauge that will give you a reading on the inner functioning of your mind and body.

- Do not use MRT to prove anything, as your belief system can interfere.

- Remain as neutral as possible with an attitude of: "I really want to know."

- The person being tested is to take responsibility for the testing.

- Always treat the body with respect. Don't argue over any test.

- Everyone using MRT professionally must keep themselves in balance to do the most accurate testing.

- Sometimes your body may not want to uncover the truth about something because its comfort zone is threatened.

- If the water level in the body being tested is very low, it can interfere with the neuro-electrical communication system in the body.

- Always do a strong test following a weak test.

- You can practice MRT with a skilled Kalos Health Facilitator for best results.

Participants Page

1. Practice determining a weak test from a strong test by using one of the methods listed:

  1) Correct name vs. incorrect name.
  2) Negative emotion vs. Strong test.
  3) Bilateral stance vs. Homolateral stance.

2. Test the three major electrical circuits. If one tests weak, correct it by rubbing the point(s) and then retest to insure it is now strong. Continue testing and balancing until all three circuits test strong.

3. Practice the "Water test" to see if water is needed for accurate testing.

Chapter Eight

Finding Trapped Emotions to Heal the Cause

For years, medical science has yearned not only to alleviate a patient's ailment, but also to understand the cause of their problem. Too often "the cure" is unknown because the *medical cause*[16] is not known. How discouraging it must be to diagnose a disease and tell the patient, "You will have to learn to live with the problem because the cause is unknown." The body is an amazing healing mechanism that can usually heal itself if the *cause* is removed. You can break into the vicious sick cycle and look through eyes of understanding. (Review the Vicious Cycle, *Chapter Seven*, *A New Day In Healing*.)

Now that you are familiar with Muscle Response Testing, you can learn how to uncover trapped emotions to reveal the hidden *cause* of a problem. Everyone has trapped emotions from earlier times. Identifying them, using MRT, helps you expose the core event, people involved, age of the onset, etc. Often you will find that underlying judgments and deceptions have created the initial cause. These deceptions can turn into immature

---

[16]See Glossary.

emotional patterns that lead to dis-ease. In every case of chronic illness, I find trapped emotions hiding the cause.

You will be uncovering trapped emotions, finding their cause, and learning how to clear them out of your body. Since emotions rely upon your thoughts and beliefs, the way to change them is to "see clearly" what is hidden there. The thought or belief that is creating the unwanted emotion is revealed.

Broken natural laws, guilt, judgments (drawing a conclusion before all of the evidence is in), and unspoken trapped emotions are at the core of most people's problems. Negative emotions are contrived from false judgments stemming from misconceptions. Seeing the truth (what is so) can release you! These techniques are based upon the scriptural adage, "Know the truth, and the truth will set you free."

Trigger Point Testing Reveals Trapped Emotions in Your Body

The following diagrams illustrate nine of the many Emotion Points available. I have found these nine to take care of enough information to complete a healing process because all emotions attach to each other like crabs on a rock. Even love and hate can be a part of the same cluster. The more emotions cluster together, the more intense they become. I used these Emotion Points to develop my work on tracing problems to their cause.

Emotion Points

1. Deep-rooted fear
2. Frustration
3. Overwhelming burden
4. Suppressed anger
5. Self image
6. Jealousy/envy
7. Resentment/control
8. Need for approval
9. Judgment/guilt

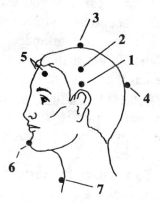

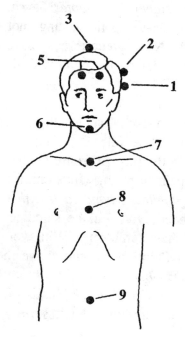

With a partner, you can test these Emotion Points on each other to see which ones are in balance. Always test with a positive attitude of: "This trigger point is in balance." Never think in your mind, "Is this point weak?" Mental thoughts can interfere with accurate muscle testing. <u>Stay neutral during the testing</u>. Don't be invested in whether a point is weak or strong. Always expect a strong test, then accept what you find.

To prepare for testing, make sure your Three Electrical Circuits are balanced and follow the instructions for accurate MRT, as shown in *Chapter Seven*. Make sure you have a fit muscle to do the testing, not weak, tired, injured, or painful. Now, you are ready to test each of the Emotion Points by touching the point with the tips of your fingers and using MRT.

To Test, point to each Trigger Point marked on the previous diagram. Use all your fingers stretched out together, as long as the finger tips are facing the point, not the flat of your finger or palm. (Illustration on next page.) *Always use your dominant hand to test their muscle.* If you are right-handed, you will be standing on their left side and testing their left arm. With your other hand lightly touch each Point, beginning above the ear (Deep-Rooted Fear). *Remember to press slowly until the muscle "locks in" and feels like a brick wall.* If their arm is bouncing, you are using too much pressure.

Assessing your findings - If all the Trigger Points test strong, it means that you are emotionally in balance at this present time. Please understand this does not mean that you do not have any trapped emotions in your body. This only means that in general, for this moment, you are clear. Later you will learn how to place an event or person in your electrical circuitry and uncover those trapped emotions. You can learn to test trapped emotions at any age. Every experience is held in the memory banks of your body, past and present. MRT helps you access them.

Weak tests indicate you have some emotional clearing to do. You will be speaking out your trapped emotions to the image of whomever is involved to clear them, while holding special points on your forehead.

Neuro-vascular Holding Points Support Inner Healing for Permanent Results

Neuro-vascular Holding Points are found over the frontal eminence bones on the upper part of the forehead. When you feel sadness, frustration, anger, etc., holding these points, while relating the upset, begins to release emotions from a subconscious level.

Dr. George Goodheart, considered the father of kinesiology, taught this technique in a "Touch for Health" sponsored seminar, stating that the natural area to place one's hands when in an upset is over the forehead. I call this technique "Speaking Out" and describe it fully on the following page.

Any time emotions surface, you can hold these points. You always use them during a Kalos Process, while speaking all of your feelings out loud to the image of the person involved. Much of what has been discovered in Applied Kinesiology has come out of observing what we do naturally. How natural it is to place one's hand over one's forehead when under stress. Could this be part of our body's survival instinct to care for ourselves?

In my research, I have repeatedly found that placing your hand over the Neuro-vascular Holding Points markedly improves the effectiveness of The Kalos Process. Without this "laying on of hands" the emotions do not release from a deep level; instead, The Process would require redoing several times. Also, the lightly held hands on the forehead are soothing and reassuring.

"Speaking out" to Clear Trapped Emotions

While holding the Neuro-vascular Holding Points, speak out your emotions in private. They are founded upon a perpetration (lie). Though you may think someone else caused you to feel the way you do, you will find that when the truth is known - *your* reactions[17] to others are part of *your* early childhood programming, not what some-one is doing to you now.

Another's behavior simply acts as a catalyst to bring up unhealed areas of your life. As an example: If you hold a belief that you are not understood, you will react to someone who has difficulty in understanding you. You may frustratingly accuse them of not paying attention or even listening to you. Yet, when the truth is known, you find that your reaction was from an experience at age five when mother was too busy to listen to you, not the person with you today! And you will keep making others wrong and accusing them, as if they were Mom and you were five years old! This is why I recommend that you — *share only feelings, not judgmental thoughts,* directly to the ones involved. Observe whether you are owning your own feelings or blaming others for feeling the way you do. Suppressed feelings turn into emotions that come out sideways (as an attitude) and affect the people around you.

Every emotion begins with a feeling that was judged and suppressed. By speaking out your feelings when in the experience of feeling them, you are less likely to judge and

---

[17]*Reaction* - See Glossary.

suppress them. Therefore, speaking your feelings is always appropriate and valuable, as long as you don't get into blaming and the Three C's: criticism, complaining, and condemning. Blaming is sharing your judgment, not sharing feelings, which supports you to own your life.

Reserve emotional clearing for private processing, not dumping sessions on those who love you. Your mind does not know the difference between the actual person being there and the image. Therefore, you can do the emotional clearing without continuing the untruth and upsetting another person with *your* programmed reaction. This way, you are taking responsibility for your life and owning your own problems, not blaming someone else!

The main purpose for emotional clearing is to *create the space* for the truth to show up. Only as you release the emotional blocks can you change the mental programming. Your mind can become so cluttered with what it believes (and is sure) is true that there is absolutely no space even to imagine anything could be different.

Emotions carry heavy pressures and judgments. Speaking out releases those tensions trapped in your body, especially in the throat, where many communication problems begin. Speaking out relieves enough stress to create the possibility that another person's viewpoint may have some credence. Possibilities show up that were impossible before, as when you are cluttered with emotions, opinions and beliefs about a situation; you are not open to discovering the truth about it. Speaking releases these held emotions and creates space for the truth to be seen and understood.

I call this a Living Process, because you can apply the different techniques of the Process in your daily life. Owning your reactions, sharing your feelings and telling the truth can "up-level" your relationships and support you to achieve your goals.

How to Speak Out While Holding
the Neuro-vascular Holding Points

1. Lightly hold the frontal eminence bones, just firmly enough to stretch the top layer of skin away from the middle of the forehead. You can hold your own points, or you may want to ask for assistance.

2. Hold your other hand over the back of the head, when the issue seems to connect to something that happened deep in the past, before memory.

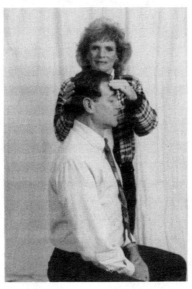

Holding the palm of your hand over the back of the head will help you access past time information. Holding your forehead and back of your head is enough to find and release all the vital information to support your clearing.

Prevent Emotional Blocks from Accumulating

You can speak out your frustrations while holding your Neuro-vascular Holding Points anytime you feel stressed. A mental review on what is bothering you, while holding these points, can give immediate relief. Speaking your feelings and frustrations out loud is best. Speaking them silently is acceptable, when speaking out loud would be difficult. Sharing your [true] feelings with others on a regular basis will prevent the need to process them later!

To avoid creating future emotional blocks, allow yourself to *experience how you feel* (when you feel that way). After identifying your feelings, practice expressing them appropriately. *"Say how you feel and ask for what you want." "Don't demand it,"* as Ken Keyes teaches in *"Rx for Happiness."*

• **Feelings furnish quality to life.** Feelings are a "now experience," bringing a scent of freshness. They grant us deep appreciation for the beauties of life. They support the luscious artist in all of us to fashion excellence from the mundane. *Feelings are the language of the soul, the primary means of communicating heart to heart.* Though everyone has a different story to tell, a different belief to share, all have felt the same feelings - no misunderstanding there. Feelings kindle the curiosity of a child and ignite the passion of consuming love. Feelings are centered in the heart (subconscious mind), yet sensed throughout our entire body.

Share Feelings before They Mutate into Emotions

• **Feelings expand and turn into strong emotional reactions if they are resisted.** *Feelings are different from emotions, yet turn into emotions as they are judged.* Feelings that are judged and resisted become emotional stress that gets stuck in the body, causing a vicious cycle of energy, creating tension wherever they collect. Resistance to feeling our feelings comes from not wanting to be uncomfortable or to *feel* a certain way. Resisting a feeling produces a judgment of: "Who or what is making me feel so bad?" As soon as you blame someone or something for how you feel, it changes into an emotion. Anger and resentment are automatic reactions to blame.

• **Understanding why people have a difficult time expressing their feelings**. Pleasers have a tendency to push their feelings down and not share them. The thought of making waves might bring dreaded rejection. When feelings get pushed down into a gut level, molehills can turn into mountains.

Some people are so much into their emotions that the emotions are having them, not the person having the emotions. They are likely to deny that they are in a mood. A

161

strong emotional reaction can create emotional dyslexia, causing a detachment from feelings. Dyslexia makes it difficult to identify what emotions are present, or what is really going on. For example, you can have a quick angry flush that covers a hurt about something that was just said. Anger might be easier to handle than hurt, because it gives a sense of control or power, while sharing your hurt may be a humbling experience too embarrassing to handle. Anger brings the possibility of controlling another person to avoid the vulnerability of opening your heart. One way to tell if a person is out of touch with their feelings is by the way they speak. They think their feelings by saying, *"I think I feel like . . .,"* or *"I feel that you . . ."* They don't just say, "I feel . . .," when sharing a feeling.

• Say *how you feel,* then *ask for what you want,* **without demanding it**. The first step in sharing how you feel is to *identify what you feel.* Simply feel what you actually feel. You can get in touch with your feelings before your pro-gramming takes over.

The second step is to notice that sharing how you feel is an expression about you, not a statement about someone else. What do you say after you say, "I feel?"

I feel sad; I feel confused; I feel discouraged; I feel hurt; I feel insecure; I feel . . .

Notice if you share your feelings with words that ex-press *thoughts* of others, instead of *feelings* of your own.

162

I feel you aren't thoughtful or fair.
I feel like you don't appreciate me.

Pure feelings do not: criticize, complain or condemn. There is no judgement or blame. Sharing pure feelings is just about you, how **you** *feel* inside, not about what you *think* about someone else.

The Third Step is to *clarify what you want, then ask without demanding it*. Asking for what you want begins the process of being the subject of your feelings not the object of them. You move from being the object (at the effect) of something you have feelings about to making a request for something you want (e.g., taking responsibility).

I feel hurt and misunderstood; what I want is to be understood clearly, so our love will deepen.

Asking for somebody to be different from whom they are is unfair and demanding. Never ask the other person to change. To uncover your want, ask yourself: "What do I want in my life that would be satisfied by them being different?" Such as, "I want to feel closer to my partner." Don't say, "I feel completely trashed; what I want is for you to treat me with more respect." Complaining about another's behavior will seldom inspire change. More likely, it will produce resistance.

• *Choice* **creates the difference between** *responding in a feeling* **way or emotionally reacting**. When you pause long enough to notice how you feel, you then can choose what to do next. The better you get at identifying your feelings (while having them), the easier you can identify an emotion when it starts to "have you." If you discover it is too late and you are already angry, identify the source of the anger (a hurt). Have compassion for yourself for hurting. Share the hurt in a non-blaming way and you will discover that you can stay in charge, instead of your emotions taking control. Profound thoughts and deep feelings make great partners in manifesting your full potential of being.

The following page lists some emotions and feelings to serve you in being aware of what you are authentically feeling in the moment. The positive feelings are in **bold**. Sharing positive feelings opens the door to sharing all your feelings maturely.

Delightful feelings to you!

COMMON FEELINGS

Abandoned	**Enthusiastic**	**Open**
Adventuresome	Envious	**Optimistic**
Agreeable	**Excited**	Pained
Alienated	Exhausted	**Peaceful**
Angry	Fearful	Pessimistic
Annoyed	Frantic	**Proud**
Anxious	Frightened	Puzzled
Apathetic	Frustrated	Regretful
Assured	**Grateful**	**Relieved**
Awkward	Guilty	Repulsed
Bashful	**Happy**	Resentful
Belittled	Helpless	Sad
Blissful	**Hopeful**	**Satisfied**
Bored	Hostile	**Self-reliant**
Calm	**Humble**	Shame
Caring	Humiliated	Shocked
Cautious	Hurt	Shy
Cheerful	Hysterical	Sorry
Compassionate	Indifferent	Spacy
Confident	**Innocent**	**Strong**
Confused	**Interested**	Stubborn
Connected	Intimidated	Stuck
Curious	Jealous	**Supported**
Daring	Lonely	**Sure**
Depressed	Lost	**Surprised**
Determined	**Loved**	Suspicious
Disappointed	**Mischievous**	Tormented
Discouraged	Miserable	Trapped
Disgusted	Mistreated	Uncertain
Embarrassed	Misunderstood	Withdrawn
Empty	Numb	Worried
Encouraged	Offended	Wounded

165

Survival Mechanisms for Me, Myself and I
Or "How to Hide My Feelings from Myself"

For the mind to survive in an intimidating world we all acquire a set of *habitual* and *unconscious defensive devices*. These survival mechanisms bolster our sense of self acceptance and "self rightness" when handling anxiety, guilt, or emotionally threatening situations. Ego Defenses alleviate post traumatic stress; soften failure or disappointment; reduce frustration and emotional conflict and protect us against acting out dangerous impulses.

In our early development stages these coping and adjusting behaviors are predictable and to some extent even healthy. As we mature, we are invited to shed defensive escape mechanisms and face our difficulties directly to attain a rich, meaningful life. Maturation is all about stopping one's avoidance of discomfort or hiding from our feelings and being open to know the truth - the very truth that sets us free.

The invitation is to be honest with yourself and others - to say how you feel and ask for what you want. When maturity does not replace these defense mechanisms, conflict continues between our id (instincts), ego, and super ego - Me, Myself and I.

"Me" instinctively knows what's best.
"Myself" is doubtful about "Me," if "Me" causes any embarrassment or discomfort to "Myself," and "I" must make sure that "Myself" and "Me" are right, proper or justified, or be punished!

These defense mechanisms are innocent enough in moderation, but when they become so powerful that they control you, problems occur.

Self-deception, denial and distortion
creates more problems than they solve.

If you rationalize away your mistakes or blame them on others, you will likely have difficulty in your career and relationships. You are not your mind, so you can choose for yourself what is real and truthful in any situation. Ploys to avoid discomfort will always plague us as long as we have a need to be comfortable, but they don't have to control our lives.

Common Ploys in Avoiding Reality

A few of the basic defensive mechanisms are defined below. Along with each is a playful quote that might have been made by a young person who was unable to deal with their anger at being caught in a "no no" and their guilt in being "unjustifiably" angry. As you can imagine, this fictitious person was not likely in touch with the anger, the guilt, or the defense being used to avoid either of them.[18]

1. *Repression* —   *"What? Naa... I don't know what you mean!"*

---

[18] The idea for this format came from *An Incomplete Education*, Chapter Nine, Psychology - by Judy Dones and William Wilson.

Repression is the root of all defense mechanisms. Repressing stressful memories is simply - blissfully forgetting. It is not to notice or not remember, unless the repressed material resurfaces. Repressed emotions are not lost, but stored in the unconscious.

2. ***Denial*** — *"MAD? You must be crazy. I'm not MAD at Mommy."*

Denial is the falsification of reality, the flip side of repression. Whereas repression distances the ego from internal anxiety, denial severs it from outside emotional pressures. Though the fantasy of denial is perfectly normal in children, it could lead to problems in adults and could suggest mental illness.

3. ***Sublimation*** — *"Mad at Mommy? Excuse me. I really must get my painting done."*

Of all the mechanisms of defense, this is the only partially helpful one. This happens when we swap an unacceptable impulse or drive for socially acceptable behavior. This process of transmuting libidinal instincts into art as opposed to gastric acids, is the source of many creative, scientific, and cultural activities.

4. ***Reversal*** — *"Angry at Her? She's mad at ME!"*

Along with repression, this is one of the first deceptions we ever used. The young ego used reversal to take the blame off self and place it where we would not be affected.

Remember in first grade: "You're stupid - no *you're* stupid - no *you're* stupid!" It is very much like projection.

5. *Projection* — *"Uh,ahw. . . I'm not mad at Mommy, DADDY is mad at Mommy."*

This is a form of projecting our unwanted emotions on someone else. Blaming others for personal shortcomings and attributing to others our own unacceptable impulses or desires sets us free from feeling our own guilt. In classical projection, a person is unaware of possessing a particular trait and projects it onto another person. "I do not get angry easily. He does." To the same degree repression ignores the emotion, projection gets rid of it by pushing it onto another person.

6. *Displacement* — *"Mad at Mommy? I've had it with Teddy bear. Bad Teddy!"*

A person expresses a feeling toward one person or object that in fact should be expressed toward another person or object. The unwanted emotion is transferred from a threatening person to a safe one with no reprisal. The feeling remains the same but the target is changed. For example, a woman who is angry with her boss may come home and displace this against the kids; or a man who has lost his wife may lavish love on his children.

7. *Reaction Formation* — *"Mad at Mommy? I ADORE Mommy! Wonder what I will make her?"*

Here impulses are denied by demonstrating the opposite extreme. To avoid true feelings, someone might even become a doting pleaser of a disliked person. A long-term reaction formationer (obsessive-compulsive) becomes excessively solicitous of the persons he or she hates or dislikes, often making elaborate ceremonial acts to keep feelings at a distance.

8. *Regression* — *"Oou, dabba dabba doo."*

Regression is reverting to an earlier age of development when life was easier. Gaining sympathy or avoiding problems can bring more comfort than handling present circumstances. This does not mean a person will use "baby talk"; it's just that his ego wants to face the situation when things were easier.

9. *Intellectualization* — *"Well, of course I'm mad at Mommy. I'm probably wishing she would go away and never come back. This is normal at my age."*

Overly explaining a problem to avoid connecting with the emotions involved, brings one to safety again. This rationalizing is a simple exchange of "thoughts about something" for anxious emotions with it. Intellectualizing isolates you from your emotions, to escape the feeling of your feelings.

"Be here now - with what is."
"Say how you feel and ask for what you want!"

Highlights

- You can learn how to uncover trapped emotions to reveal the hidden *cause* of a problem.

- MRT is used for testing emotions trapped in the body. Identifying trapped emotions helps you expose the core event, people involved, age of the onset, etc. to find and heal the cause.

- Negative emotions are contrived from false judgments stemming from misconceptions.

- The Kalos Process is based upon the scriptural adage, "Know the truth and the truth will set you free."

- Trigger Point testing reveals trapped emotions in your body. The Nine Emotion Points to test are:

  1. Deep-rooted fear
  2. Frustration
  3. Overwhelming burden
  4. Suppressed anger
  5. Self image
  6. Jealously/envy
  7. Resentment/control
  8. Need for approval
  9. Judgment/guilt

- To prepare for testing, make sure your Three Electrical Circuits are balanced.

- To Test, point to each Trigger Point with your non-dominant hand, using the tips of your fingers.

- You can clear yourself of trapped emotions any time using the Neuro-vascular holding points on the forehead.

- Holding the palm of your hand over the back of your head will help you to access past time information.

- Speaking out your trapped emotions will create the space for the truth to show up and for resolution to take place.

- Reserve emotional clearing for Processing, not dumping sessions on those who love you.

- Speaking out emotions relieves stress and creates the possibility that another person's viewpoint may have some credence.

- Feelings are a "now experience," bringing a scent of freshness. They grant us deep appreciation for the beauties of life.

- Feelings are the language of the soul, a primary means of communicating heart to heart.

- You can tell if a person is out of touch with their feelings by the way they speak, by saying, *"I think I feel like ..., or I feel that you ...,"* instead of saying, "I feel..."

- Being able to share your feelings is a sign of maturity.

- Feelings expand and turn into strong emotional reactions if they are resisted.

- Choice creates the difference between responding in a feeling way or reacting emotionally. **Pause** long enough to notice how you feel, then **choose** what to do next.

- Our minds have survival mechanisms to hide or avoid our feelings. For the mind to survive in an intimidating world we all acquire a set of *habitual* and *unconscious defensive devices*.

  1. Repression   6. Displacement
  2. Denial   7. Reaction Formation
  3. Sublimation   8. Regression
  4. Reversal   9. Intellectualization
  5. Projection

- Defense mechanisms are normal in a young child, but become a hindrance to mature adult behavior.

- Avoiding reality involves denial, self-deception and/or distortion that creates more problems than it solves.

- "Say how you feel and ask for what you want!"

- Survival mechanisms are at the foundation of dyslexia. When the mind goes into an escape mode and goes

blank, the left and right hemispheres of the brain disconnect, causing immature defensive behavior.

Participants Page

1. <u>Memorize and practice</u> testing the nine emotion points. Record below and check the weak ones.

   1.   6.
   2.   7.
   3.   8.
   4.   9.
   5.

2. <u>List and speak out</u> all of the trapped emotions relating to an area of your life that feels fearful or insecure that could get in the way of your achieving a goal for your life. Notice how emotions cling to each other. Hold the Neuro-vascular Holding Points on your forehead while speaking.

3. <u>Practice sharing intimate feelings</u>. What was your most embarrassing moment? Tell someone close to you about the event. Notice how well you express your feelings vs. think your feelings.

4. Think about accomplishing a specific goal - asking for a raise or getting up in front of a large audience. Then, test the Emotion Points. Speak Out your feelings toward whoever would be involved.

Chapter Nine

Understanding and Testing for Emotional Dyslexia

An emotional upset can cause one to go mentally blank or confused. When emotional overwhelm interferes with logical and rational behavior, one will usually find that the left and right hemispheres of the brain are not functioning simultaneously. This condition is called dyslexia. You become either super logical or super emotional. There is not the natural holistic viewpoint coming from being integrated in both thoughts and feelings; or as some would state it, "From the left to the right sides of the brain."

Emotional dyslexia is not to be confused with "learning dyslexia." They appear and act very similar. Learning dyslexia happens when the right and left hemispheres of the brain disconnect while in a learning process. Learning dyslexia can cause one to transpose letters, numbers, have reading problems with speed and comprehension, can have difficulty in determining right from left directions.

The correction for learning dyslexia is very similar to the correction for emotional dyslexia. A complete dyslexia examination and all of the components necessary for correction are contained in Book Three, "*The Manual*" of this series. For our purposes the following will suffice.

177

Mental/emotional Overload Causes "Switching Off" of Right/left Brain, Making Problem Solving Difficult

When experiencing emotional dyslexia, one is not functioning with both hemispheres of the brain simultaneously, so resolving problems is difficult. The best of intentions to express love, kindness and compassion may be unattainable. One can become trapped by the dyslexic condition, causing an over-reaction.

For example, at the time of an emotional upset, whatever is in your immediate environment - smell, taste, sights and sounds can become programmed into your memory banks as part of the threat. People, food, animals, present at this time can show up later in the form of automatic irrational behavior or as an allergic reaction.

You may have been frightened by a dog at the age of two while holding an ice cream cone and standing in dry grass. Your mind can program "ice cream" in with the fear, causing an allergy to ice cream. Even the dry grass or pollens present may be a part of the automatic reaction. In the future a new situation (with a dog, dry grass or ice cream) could bring up the same programmed reaction and mysteriously leave you feeling as disjointed as you did then, though no real threat exists.

Becoming emotionally dyslexic at holidays is very common and around certain people who trigger fear or insecurity. When circumstances or situations come up with any kind of threat attached, one side of the brain "switches off." You can become very emotional or confused when your logical left brain shuts down. When your right brain shuts down you feel detached from your feelings and find it difficult to communicate heart to heart.

When mentally or emotionally overloaded, anyone can switch off one side of the brain or the other. Since most chronic problems in the present have roots in the past, the old programming comes up over and over again in need of healing.

Some People Go into a Left Brain Mode - <u>Analytical Dominance</u>

When in a "left brain mode" you experience a separation from your feelings. People may complain that you are cold, distant, or in denial of your feelings. The truth of the matter is that you do have feelings, but connecting with them is difficult because of the perceived emotional threat.

Other People Go into a Right Brain Mode - <u>Emotional Dominance</u>

When your "left brain" switches off, it is almost impossible to think rationally. Mountains are made out of molehills. You feel like you are "falling apart." Others feel they cannot reason with you because of your overwhelm and inability to be logical. When this becomes a pattern, a child may learn to manipulate his world by emotionally falling apart. He becomes unreasonable, illogical, sometimes to the point of temper tantrums or in losing touch with reality.

This does not mean emotionally dyslexic people don't experience both modes - being logical and having true feelings. It simply means they cannot do this at the same time. They may flip between logic and emotions or stay in any one mode for a prolonged period. They are probably in a balanced mode most of the time. It requires a catalyst to trigger the switching off. This condition may only arise around certain people or in certain situations.

You Can Remedy Emotional Dyslexia

You can align both hemispheres of your brain to support mature behavior through seeing the truth of the situation. Remember, ALL negative emotions have a perpetration (self-deception) attached. So, as soon as you understand the TRUTH, union takes place between both hemispheres of the brain. You can tell when The Process is finished by the peaceful feeling you now have with the previous problem.

♦ *Both sides of the brain are used in The Process.*
The use of "left brain logic" and "languaging," and "right brain images" and "inner sensing," creates connection between right and left sides of the brain, creating the integration that you didn't have at the time of the initial upset.

♦ *Both sides of the brain are aligned through The Kalos Process.* (See Section III)

Uncovering the unconscious deception aligns both *thoughts* and *feelings*, so the mind can function in a balanced way - wholistically.

♦ *The ability to use both sides of the brain simultaneously (thoughts and feelings) supports future mature behavior.*

I call this, "a wholistic way of functioning." We all have feelings, whether we can express them or not. We all have rational thoughts, though our behavior may appear irrational at times. It is when you align both your thoughts and feelings in a mature way that you achieve results in every area of your life.

Testing for Emotional Dyslexia

You will be using two symbols for testing dyslexia. An "**X**" symbol is used to represent left and right brain connection. Two parallel lines "**II**" is the symbol that represents the left and right brain not being connected. Make sure that the parallel lines are long enough to look like railroad tracks. Using the short characters of an eleven for the parallel lines will not work. See Participants Page for an example.

Since you will be using MRT, please re-familiarize yourself with the hints for accurate testing. Begin by making sure that your Three Electrical Circuits are in balance, then proceed with a testing partner.

1. On a piece of paper draw a large bold "**X**" (four inches or larger). While your partner looks at the "**X**" do a muscle response test on them. Always look for a strong.

✓ If the "**X**" tests *strong*, it means that the brain is integrated with both sides working simultaneously.

✓ If the "**X**" tests *weak*, the left and right sides of the brain are not connected at this moment.

2. To double-check your test, draw two parallel lines the same size as the previous symbol. Have your testing partner look at the "**‖**" (railroad tracks) and use MRT.

✓ If the "**‖**" tests *strong*, it means only one hemisphere of the brain is working at a time.

✓ If the "**‖**" tests *weak*, it means that the brain is connected, as when the "**X**" is strong.

A correct test will always have one *strong*, and one *weak*. When the "**X**" test is *strong*, the "**‖**" symbol should always test weak. With any conflicting tests, such as both testing strong or both testing weak, recheck:

If both symbols test *strong*, you may not be using enough pressure in the test. If both are *weak*, you may be using too much pressure.

Testing for Emotional Dyslexia in Relation to Someone or Some Situation

As you become more adept at using this technique, you can learn how to uncover information useful for both revealing the cause of problems and supporting you to be your optimum in relation to life's challenges. In any situation, you can test to see if one side of the brain is switched off. You can also test to see if you go into emotional dyslexia around specific people, i.e., a spouse, boss; or in roles you play, i.e., mother, manager; or in circumstances you face, i.e., teaching, lecturing, getting accurate reports in on time.

Choose something you want to test for dyslexia, i.e., a general role such as, a relationship. In this sample you will be testing if you are integrated left and right brain when in relationship with someone. You can narrow your focus and test for dyslexia around a specific person or use a general subject like "relationship."

State a specific person or situation in the circuit using a muscle response test. Then, have your partner look at the "X" and test again. Simply by stating something in the electrical circuitry of the body and testing immediately afterwards places it in the body's memory system. Practice the following by stating out loud:

✓ *"Relationship with ____ in the circuit,"*
Test immediately.
　　"Circuits in the Clear." MRT again.
✓ Testing Partner looks at "**X**" and you test again.

183

✓ Testing Partner looks at "**II**" and you test again. (Remember to do a strong test after any weak test.)

By making the statement: *"Circuits in the Clear"* and using MRT you are making sure that the statement ("Relationship in the circuit") did not "blow out" your electrical circuits. Often, when something is placed in your body's circuitry that has emotional trauma attached, your electrical system will go into overload. This causes a short circuit in one or more of your three major circuits. Do not be discouraged by this, just rub the circuits and retest. On the next page you will learn exercises to support your integration and prevent electrical blowouts in the future. So, always make the statement, "Circuits in the clear" after stating something into the circuitry.

✓ A *strong* test confirms that the circuits are in balance. In the event of a *weak* test it means that you must re-balance the circuit that is out, retest.

✓ If looking at the "X" tests strong and looking at the "**II**" tests weak you are integrated left and right brain in relationship to the person or situation in the statement.

✓ If the "X" test is weak and the "**II**" test is strong you are emotionally dyslexic in this situation.

184

Testing for Emotional Dyslexia at Any Age

You can place any age in the circuit just as you did with relationship. You might want to go to the first time you had a right/left brain integration problem.

✓ Simply state, "*Age ___ in the Circuit*" and use MRT.
Look at the "X" and test.
Look at the "**II**" and test.

✓ If the "X" tests *strong*, you were integrated at that age. If when looking at "**II**" you test *strong* with that age in the circuit it means you were not integrated from a left-right brain perspective.

Exercises to Integrate Your Left and Right Brain — Thoughts and Feelings

There are brain integration exercises to realign this "switching-off" problem and to support the body's ability to stay aligned. We use these exercises for Learning Dyslexia as well as Emotional Dyslexia. These exercises can be used anytime, and are most helpful when used after the Kalos Process to support newly corrected information to permeate your mind. Of course, unless you understand the cause of a problem, a permanent clearing will be difficult and reappearance inevitable.

The left brain controls the right side of the body and the right brain controls the left side of the body. Thus, when you do these three bilateral exercises, you are reinforcing the body–mind connection by requiring a continuous neuro-electrical flow between left and right hemispheres of the brain. During the exercises, groups of muscles turn on and off while moving the eyes, humming and focusing one's thoughts upon a truthful statement. This creates harmony, while integrating one's true thoughts and feelings.

One lady told me how wonderful it was to again experience deep love for her husband, whom she was considering leaving because of the distance she was feeling. After a Kalos Process she began doing these exercises daily and much to her surprise, her love grew deeper and deeper. She felt different after every session of exercising and declaring "her truth" into being. Her statement of truth was: "I love my husband and choose a happy, fulfilling relationship with him." She was able to experience what it was to be with her husband without going dyslexic! I am amazed at how many people go dyslexic around someone they love!

Using Declarations with the Integration Exercises

Each exercise has a declaration attached to it. "*I take responsibility for my life,*" is one for the first exercise. You can use any truthful statement that you would like.

Using these statements will increase brain integration and facilitate specific success in any area of choice.

You can make up your own statement. What's important is to state "your truth." Do not say something that you would like to believe, but don't. Declare something that you believe to be true right now! This requires introspection. The statement you make up and use during the exercise will help you integrate what you already believe into subconscious programming. How often do you say one thing, only to admit later that you have a difficult time living up to that belief? Brain Integration Exercises will help you achieve success and win at walking your talk.

Three Brain-Integration Exercises

1. Cross Crawl Exercise

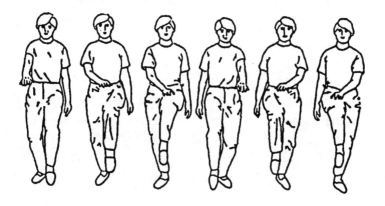

a. Do a walking in place exercise holding your head level, looking straight ahead with arms swinging, touching your left knee with your right hand and vice versa.

b. Declare: *"I take responsibility for my life."*

c. To add to the effectiveness of the exercise, hum as you image your declaration. What does taking responsibility for your life look like and feel like? Make it a positive experience. This statement is especially strengthening to the circulation and sexual organs.

d. Keeping your head level; now move your eyes in a large circle, as if you were looking at a clock which is as big as the room. Pause slightly at each number on the clock to make sure you keep the circle round. Rotate eyes in both directions several times.

2. Side to Side Exercise

a. Extend your right arm and left leg out in opposite directions, as pictured. A little jump as you do this makes it easier to keep your arm and leg in opposite positions. This is an especially good exercise to strengthen the pancreas and any weaknesses caused from worrying.

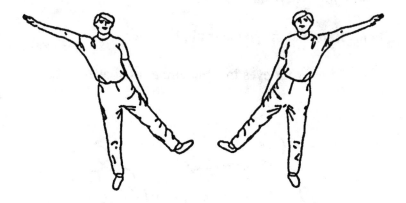

b. Declare: *"I relax and do my best."*

c. Hum and image the truth, as above.

d. Move your eyes in a big circle, as above.

3. Front to Back Exercise

a. Take a step backwards. Stretch the same side of your body in opposite directions by placing your right arm forward and your right leg backward. Touch your opposite thigh with the hand that goes to the back of your body. If you will pass the mid-line of your body, it will increase its effectiveness. This exercise is especially good for people with colon problems, liver problems, or not learning from the past.

189

b. Declare: *"I Joyously release the past and make way for beneficial change."*

c. Hum and image the truth, as above.

d. Move your eyes in a big circle, as above.

These various additions to the exercises reach many parts to the brain and integrates the left and right sides to function simultaneously. Humming and rolling your eyes in a circle help to integrate the information into the various brain cells that have been switched off. You only need to do this two or three minutes, once or twice a day, to see results. Try it. You'll love the results!

Highlights

- Dyslexia is a situation where only one hemisphere of the brain can function at a time. Therefore, you become either super-logical or super-emotional.

- Even the best of intentions to express love and kindness become unattainable, which makes problem solving very difficult.

- A left brain mode is very analytical and logical. People may complain that you are cold, distant, or in denial of your feelings.

- A right brain mode can be very emotional and "mountains can be made out of molehills."

- Mental or emotional overload can cause the "switching off" process.

- You can dissolve emotional dyslexia and align both sides of the brain through seeing the truth of the situation.

- The Kalos Process accesses both sides of the brain and brings them into unity.

- Having the ability to use both sides of the brain simultaneously supports mature behavior.

- You can test for emotional dyslexia through MRT:
  Look at a big "X" while testing your muscle.
  A weak test shows you are dyslexic in that moment.
  A strong test means you are not.

- You can reaffirm your testing by looking at a railroad track, like an extra long eleven, while being tested.

- You can test the body at any age by stating the age in the circuit.

- There are three exercises to align your thoughts and feelings into unity. They are called Brain Integration Exercises. They re-educate your body, mind, and right and left brain patterns into one.

  1. Cross Crawl Exercise
  2. Side to Side Exercise
  3. Front to Back Exercise

- Declarations support the integration of reality into the memory banks of the mind to reprogram the subconscious mind.

- You can make up your own statement, just make sure that it is a true statement that you already believe on a conscious level.

- Humming and rolling your eyes in a circle help to integrate the information into the various brain cells that have been switched off.

Participant's Page

1. Test to see if at this time you are integrated left and right brain using the "X" and the railroad tracks. If not, test at what age this general pattern of emotional dyslexia began. Do the "Brain Integration Exercises," using an appropriate statement.

2. Place a situation or relationship with a special person in the circuit and test for emotional dyslexia.

3. With that situation or relationship in the circuit, test the nine emotion points found in *Chapter Eight*.

You are simply practicing the technique for later use in The Kalos Process for Resolving the Cause. If there is a pattern of dyslexia, it is important to establish when it began. The exercises will begin to strengthen your ability to respond more successfully around those persons and situations.

Chapter Ten

Aligning the Double Mind for Success

Thinking One Way and Feeling the Other

Often, we only *think* that we want to heal ourselves. Yet, on a subconscious level, we *feel* that we don't. This is what I call a "Double Mind." The conscious mind governs our thinking and accounts for about 20% of our behavior, while *80% of our behavior comes from our subconscious mind*, poetically called "the heart." How your subconscious mind feels about a problem is very important.

People are continually amazed at discovering that they only *thought* they wanted to be well, or achieve a particular goal, while 80 percent of their behavior (subconscious mind) didn't. MRT can be used to unveil the subconscious fear that was getting in the way of "single minded" achievement.

Double Mindedness Gets in the Way
of Achieving Goals

When speaking before a conference overseas, I met an athlete who was practicing to participate in their National Olympics. MRT disclosed that he was double minded about winning. He *thought* he wanted to win, but *felt* he didn't. Though surprised about the testing, he had to admit it was accurate, as he was having a hard time staying on his very strict training program. He was concerned about having the discipline required to achieve his goal.

In asking him what was getting in the way of *feeling* he wanted to win, he paused and told me that maybe it was because if he were the best, he would be like his Dad. "What is the matter with that?" I asked. "Well, my Dad has to win at everything and he is very obnoxious about it. I don't want to be like him." I reassured him that just being aware of that would give him enough wisdom to be able to be his best and still be humble. We completed The Process with outlining an optimum workout program that would support his winning. Two months later I heard the good news. He won!

Most of the time I find that people are "double minded" about their goals. This is the main reason they have not achieved them. They only believe on the surface that this is what they want, while underneath lurks a fear that keeps them stuck.

Feelings can cluster and build into a "wake-up call" in the form of a symptom letting one know they are not listening to their deeply suppressed emotions. Feelings are mainly a right brain function stemming from subconscious beliefs. Identifying suppressed feelings would be difficult without the tools of MRT.

How often do you sabotage your achievements by not being single minded about what you want? When your right and left hemispheres of the brain are aligned in thoughts and feelings, it is like a laser beam of energy is focused on your dream coming true. All the support of the universe empowers you. You can't help but win when you are aligned:

Left Brain	—	Right Brain
Thoughts	—	Feelings
Head	—	Heart
Conscious Mind	—	Subconscious Mind

A Corporate President Had Issues around Having Money and Remaining a Spiritual Man

A corporate head of several businesses, who had made fortunes in the past, found himself losing money in many of his investments. He began to wonder what was going on. I met with him and found that ever since he had become "spiritual," his monetary matters had deteriorated.

MRT showed that he was double minded about being able to be successful monetarily and yet be a devoted man of God. This was traced to beliefs that money is not spiritual. Many people test weak with the money issue because of all of the negative beliefs around it, such as "filthy lucre," dirty money, greed, abusive power, cheating, unspiritual, materialistic, etc.

During a Kalos Process he uncovered his hidden beliefs about money, resolved them, and became single minded. He became clear that money is simply a yardstick of one's labors - a value one places upon one's time. Uncovering his "perpetration" with money aligned his thoughts and feelings to accomplish his goal with ease. He went on to resolve his financial dilemma, while remaining a spiritual man in service to humanity.

Optimum success in achieving your goal
requires the alignment of thoughts and feelings.

You can easily test yourself to see if you have any issues around money. Hold a large currency bill in your hand and have someone do MRT to see if you are strong or weak. Later in this chapter you will learn how to do this double mind testing on your goals and projects.

Thinking One Way and *Feeling* Another is Common, Especially Among the Chronically Ill

I have had patients tell me that they are absolutely sure they want to heal, only to find out, through MRT, that subconsciously they actually don't. The lady in the following story had an "incurable" disease and was in constant pain.

A lovely young woman got very angry with me for revealing through MRT that she subconsciously didn't

A lovely young woman got very angry with me for revealing through MRT that she subconsciously didn't want to live. "I don't believe you," she cried. Then allowing further questioning and testing, she saw how she blamed herself for her mother's lifelong illness and early death. This of course was absurd, but real to her double mind.

Her mother had been sick all of her life and "should never" have had a child, so the daughter was told. Thus, when the little one was born her mother had serious complications. The little girl felt responsible for her mother's eventual early death and carried a heavy subconscious burden for "causing" her mother's ailment.

Through uncovering her unconscious fears and beliefs, the young woman's resistance to healing became understandable and resolvable. She took a stand to live and started a healing process in her body. She aligned her double mind and succeeded at healing the cause.

I find this double mindedness common when working with the chronically ill. When I ask questions to reveal where the double mindedness came from, I get some surprising answers. One common response the subconscious mind blurts out is: "Others would expect too much of me if I were well." Illness may be a way of escaping responsibility or avoiding having to say no, when asked to do more than you *feel* you can do. Once a patient said that if she got well, she would not take as good care of herself as she does now. What kind of rationale is this?

Fears from Early Childhood
Can Cause Double Mindedness

Sometimes our thinking is not as logical as one would expect. This is understandable when we realize that most of our subconscious beliefs are formed during the first few years of life. Many present time ailments are from programming or patterns from the past. These early fears become part of the core programming that motivates behavior.

In early childhood we set up patterns that stay with us for life. Often the patterns we take on are from past generations who were functioning from survival. Now, we can reveal and resolve those patterns through MRT. The two major areas of subconscious fears that bring up our "bottom line survival programming" are:

1. I am not loved (accepted) — right brain.
2. I am not good enough — left brain.

Both statements are founded upon a belief that, *"There is something wrong with me!"* Therefore, behind the cause of every problem is this fundamental fear. Each person has their individual way of proving this negative belief to be true. Please open to the possibility that your chronic problem is a result of believing a perpetration (a lie). The truth is: "You are good enough" and "You are loved!" MRT can help you to get to the bottom line perpetration that blocks your problem from aligning to single mindedness and resolution.

200

Common Subconscious Programming Revealed in Chronic Illnesses:

• Fear of rejection

"I would rather die than be rejected," or *"I don't want to confront this person about how I feel or they will get angry at me."* Fear of rejection is how the mind controls your behavior to keep you safe, <u>not</u> happy. A payoff for this fear is that you get to be right about not being accepted the way you are. You don't even accept yourself! Your illness proves it! All you can do is to get as much attention as possible to substitute for not feeling loved. Neediness has a way of making one feel more in control, because of all the requests attended to. A family can be ruled from a sick bed.

"The person who makes the most requests, controls the most!" Helplessness becomes powerful!

• Fear of not measuring up

"I can't do it right, anyway, so why try?" Incapability has its way of allowing you to escape responsibility. Illness allows one to prove they are right about not being good enough — "Just look at me!" And the paradox is that you get to feel a sense of power when you *overcome* a serious ailment. You get to feel good enough!

• Fear of failure

"I can't go there" or *"I can't do that."* Illness becomes a way to keep you safe from embarrassment and safe from feeling like a failure. This fear of rejection or

201

not being good enough shows up as helplessness. Low self-esteem says, "Nothing ventured, nothing to fail."

• Fear of unworthiness
   Illnesses can be used to punish yourself or another.

Blaming self: *"I don't deserve to be well, because it's*
                    unforgivable that I . . . "
Blaming others: *"Because you did/didn't ..., see what*
                    happened to me!"

   These examples are not to be used to prove you are "right" about someone who is ill. Please use insights to really understand and support a person to heal. Don't be judgmental. Because of the subconscious nature of these feelings, people are totally unaware that they exist. Their conscious mind will definitely resist them.

You Must Make a Decision to Heal

   Through MRT you can find out whether you are aligned in **wanting to be well or not.** If not aligned, you can discover "what is getting in the way." MRT gives you a way to determine what you believe in your subconscious mind. Some only *think* they want to be well or successful, but on a subconscious *feeling* level, they don't. You can become clear on whether you have made the decision to heal or not.
   You can determine whether you have another set of programming that says, "Yes, I want to be well, but I

don't believe it is possible." If your mind says that getting well is impossible for you, guess what? Your mind controls your body. Therefore, it will not allow the body to heal if it has decided that it cannot. Being sensitive to your feelings, thoughts and desires will help you resolve the blocks that could be getting in your way of wanting to be well.

Being transformed requires becoming transparent. That means that you are willing to tell the truth about your thoughts and feelings. It means that you are open to be tested on what is in your subconscious mind. The whole point is to come to understanding and wholeness. You will discover how much you have hidden, even from yourself.

Learning to Test for Double Mindedness

Your muscle works as a **lie detector test** and tells you if you are telling the truth. You can state the following "I think I . . ." and "I feel I . . ." while adding a statement to the end of each related to accomplishing a goal or project. Your body will tell you the truth of how it is programmed. Of course you would never use MRT to decide for you, as decisions are to be made through choice, not old programming tainted with fear. MRT only tells you what has been programmed into your mind and reveals a hidden agenda that needs healing.

First, Test What You WANT

Test what you *think* you want consciously and *feel* you want subconsciously. If you have a partner with you right now, make sure that both of you have your three circuits balanced. Practice a strong and weak test as described in *Chapter Six*. The person being tested makes the following statement and you slowly press down on their arm:

"I *think* I **want** to be happy." (Use MRT)
Determine if tests are weak or strong after each MRT.
"I *feel* I **want** to be happy." (Use MRT)

A strong test means the statement is true; a weak test means the statement is false. Notice if one statement tests strong and the other weak, or if both tests are of the same strength. There are four possible results for the above example:

1. Both are strong, meaning you are single minded in wanting to be happy.
2. Both are weak, meaning that you are single minded in NOT wanting to be happy.
3. The *think* part is strong and the *feel* part is weak, meaning that you consciously want to be happy, but subconsciously don't.

4. The *think* part is weak and the *feel* part is strong, meaning that you consciously do not want to be happy, but you subconsciously do.

Second, Test If You Believe You CAN

Often you may test single minded that you **want** something, only to find that you *think* and *feel* that you CANNOT have it. The following test identifies if you CAN achieve what you want.

"I *think* I **can** be happy." (Use MRT)
"I *feel* I **can** be happy." (Use MRT)

This test reveals how you relate to feeling *worthy, capable or skillful* of achieving your goals. I am amazed at how often people will test out aligned to wanting something, only to find they *think or feel* they cannot achieve it. Some *think* they don't deserve it because of doing some "unpardonable sin."

Feeling capable can be linked to a pattern of self doubt, "I don't ever seem to complete anything, so...," or "I'm not disciplined enough, so...," etc. Others will feel they do not have the skills or technical capacity that their goal requires to be achievable. You can practice how to test any statement by adding your project to "I think" and "I feel" and using MRT. Becoming clear on your objectives can also help you in becoming single minded on achieving them.

Practicing Think - Feel Testing

To determine if you are double or single minded about what you want, practice the following statements using MRT.

> *"I think I want . . ."* (add your project/goal and
> MRT)
> *"I feel I want . . ."*
> *"I think I can . . ."*
> *"I feel I can . . ."*

If you show a weak response on any test, you will want to understand where the discrepancy is — between *thoughts* and *feelings* or **"wants"** and **"cans."** Listing your goals and how you test on them is helpful when moving onto The Kalos Process in Section III. Study the following review to know where to go after the *think/feel* testing.

<u>When all the tests are strong</u>, it means that you are aligned to achieving your goal or that you are in the process of achievement. Therefore, you can take the next step in achieving that goal using another think/feel test. See if you are single minded on each stage of development in achieving your goal. You will want to go on to practice Double Mind Testing on an area that is not aligned.

<u>When all the tests are weak</u>, it means that you are out of touch with what you even want, consciously and subconsciously! This is a rare occasion and is handled in detail in Book Three, *The Manual*.

When the *think* part is strong and the *feel* part is weak, it means that you consciously want to succeed at your goal, but subconsciously you don't. This shows that you will want to ask the question: **"What is getting in the way of your *feeling* you do not want this goal?"** Use MRT to test every answer by having the person state their answer in the following way: "I *think* it is because . . ." and "I *feel* it is because . . . " and test. By continuing the testing of your *think/feel* statements, you will discover the fear at the bottom of the problem. Each weak test will expose a hidden agenda. You then can look at what is REAL and coach them through by asking more questions, showing that they are capable.

Trust your inner direction here. You can tell what makes sense and what doesn't. You can also use The Universal Principles found at the end of this text to clarify any discrepancies or perpetrations. The Universal Principles are the best guide I know to expose the inner functioning of mental precepts and principles to get to the contextual level, where the *cause* is found. See *Chapter Sixteen - Sample Processes*.

When the *think* part is weak and the *feel* part is strong, it means that you consciously do not want to achieve your goal, but you subconsciously do. You would simply ask: "What is getting in the way of your *thinking* that way?" Changing the conscious mind is usually faster and easier than changing the subconscious mind. You are not your mind, so you can change either how you *think* or how you *feel*. As an example: You *think* you do not want to change your career, yet you *feel* you do. Your logical

207

left brain may be saying, "It is most practical to stay where I am. That way, I don't take any chance of failing or being accepted in another area." This reasoning is like, "A bird in the hand is worth two in the bush." Remember, the mind's need to be right to survive is a powerful force that motivates our actions.

Most of the time the test is just the opposite, thinking you DO and feeling you DON'T. Since you are not your mind, you can decide what it is you want to change — Your *thoughts* or your *feelings*! You are the one in charge of your mind! There is a payoff for changing your career, etc., and a payoff for not. "What do you want?" is the question. Simply by feeding back questions in the form of statements, as above, and testing will bring you to alignment.

Sometimes you may have a difficult time deciding what you want. I suggest that you experiment with a choice that brings the most joy. "What are you willing to experiment with?" At least you can get on with your life mentally and emotionally aligned. Being double minded causes much frustration and anxiety. Remember, just because you make a decision about a career, doesn't mean that you cannot make another decision later. Exploring careers can be fascinating!

Create Clear Communication with your Body

Test statements the student makes after you ask the question. Do not test questions. Always make sure that strong tests mean "yes" and weak tests mean "no" to prevent confusion in the body's communication system. Either use a **positive statement** and test it or let the person being tested say a *think/feel* statement, then test. To keep communication clear always use a clear statement with no double negatives. Below is a sample Double Mind Test that places all four statements together (in a positive way) as you would in applying this technique.

"I *think* I **want** to be well." [MRT — Strong]
"I *feel* I **want** to be well." [MRT — Weak]
"I *think* I **can** be well." [MRT — Strong]
"I *feel* I **can** be well." [MRT — Weak]

This person was STRONG on both *thinking* they **wanted** to be well *and* *thinking* they **could** be well but WEAK on *feeling* they **wanted** to or *feeling* they **could** be well. This means that their conscious mind believed that they wanted to be well and could be well. The subconscious mind felt that they neither wanted to be well nor could be well. Thus the conscious mind (20%) was aligned to be well and the subconscious mind (80%) was aligned to be sick. Without resolving this double minded block, healing would be nearly impossible.

You will be able at least to confirm some of the reasons you are not aligned to achieve what you want. Often just seeing that you are double minded will get your mind's attention so much that it will feel caught and it will then surrender to "what is Reality."

In this chapter you have been learning how to test for double mindedness. In the next Chapter you will learn to identify whether there is a related problem of Emotional Dyslexia. All of the techniques presented in Section II are to assist you to become confident and skillful in testing. Then in *Section III*, you will have a step by step guide for using The Kalos Process. Through this process you can resolve the cause of the double mindedness and its related problem.

The Participant's Page at the end of this Chapter will provide you more opportunities to practice Double Mind Testing. Always go back and retest all of the previous statements to make sure they all test strong before finishing the Double Mind Processing. This assures that you are aligned to succeed.

Highlights

- You may *think* you want to heal, but *feel* you don't.

- The conscious mind accounts for about 20% of our behavior, while the subconscious mind is about 80%.

- Feelings can cluster and build into a "wake-up call" in the form of a symptom letting one know they are not listening to their deeply suppressed emotions.

- Optimum success requires the alignment of head and heart, thoughts and feelings.

- Fears from early childhood can cause double mindedness. The two major fears are: Am I accepted (loved) and am I good enough?

- The right brain wants to be loved or accepted, while the left brain wants to be good enough. You will find your problems have a double mind behind them.

- Double mindedness is common among the chronically ill. Helplessness can become powerful through realizing that: *"The person who makes the most requests, controls the most."*

- Illness can be a way of proving you are right about a fear, such as: Fear of not measuring up, fear of failure, etc.

211

- You must make a decision to heal. MRT will tell you if you are programmed to heal.

- Being sensitive to your feelings, thoughts and desires will help you to uncover and resolve the blocks that could be getting in your way of wanting to be well.

- Your muscle works as a lie detector test and tells you if you are telling the truth.

- You can test to see if you are aligned with your *thoughts* and *feelings* to have what you want in life, called single mindedness. You can get in the way of your own success by being double minded.

- When using MRT, a strong test means the statement is true and a weak test means the statement is false.

- Always begin Double Mind Testing by stating:
  I think I want . . .
  I feel I want . . . Then follow with saying:
  I think I can have . . .
  I feel I can have . . .

- Not only can you test to see if you are single minded about what you WANT. You can also test to see if you are single minded about what you believe you CAN have.

Participant's Page

1. LIST GOALS AND DO THINK/FEEL TESTING ON THEM: Think and Feel Want to; Think and Feel Can.
Examples:

    I think I want to "change my career."

    I think I want to "heal my long term problem of __."

    I think I want to "develop a ____."

    Remember also to test "I *think* I **can** ..."

2. CHECK YOUR SELF ESTEEM WITH MRT.
Examples:

    I think I like myself.

    I think I am open to share my love most of the time.

    I think my heart is open to receive love from others.

    I think I am happy most of the time.

    I think my male and female energy is integrated.

4. WRITE CLEARLY AND TEST A CORE ISSUE IN A RELATIONSHIP.
Examples:

    I think I want to share my feelings openly with
        (Use his or her name).

    I think I want to heal my relationship with ____.

    I think I want to stop reacting to (his or her). . .

SECTION III

RESOLVING THE CAUSE❣

Integrating Principles with Techniques Creating a Step by Step Guide to *Heal The Cause* through the Kalos Process

To empower people healing what was,
To live fully out of what is,
To manifest our full potential in what can be,
To co-create what will be.

Chapter Eleven

Preparing for the Kalos Process

The Original Intent

The context of The Kalos Process has been developed over the past twenty-five years; the refining of the methodology over the last thirteen. It was originally called the Relaxed Focused Attention (RFA) Process. A team of professionals gathered together to create a way to support people to achieve a transformed life and realize their spiritual goals. Realizing that our attitude is the biggest factor in determining our health and happiness, we wanted to create a process to:

Teach lay people a simple method to achieve their goals and renew their minds to a perpetual positive attitude that glorified God.

Through unveiling and forgiving the misconceptions of the past, the mind can be renewed and people's lives can be transformed! We were excited as we researched many methods to accomplish this end. The intent was to develop and teach a simple enough method for lay people to learn in a short amount of time. We wanted to apply a method whereby people could take more responsibility in their own physical, emotional and spiritual healing process safely, yet profoundly. We were amazed as we watched many long-term problems with allergies and chronic pain alleviated in one Process. We rejoiced in the experiences of unconditional love and gratitude. We knew that though we all wanted to be all that we could be, our minds would always take us back to our old "stories" that could steal our peace and joy. Therefore, The Kalos Process was designed to wake up our consciousness to "see the truth" of the matter and to stop allowing our minds to run away with us into its old outdated programming based upon fear and insecurity. Knowing how to access our "Full Potential" in any circumstance empowers us to transform our lives.

By taking a look at your life in this new way, you can find the perpetration (deception) behind the cause of any problem. Through understanding and differentiating what is real from what is false, you develop a new way to look at life's situations. You are able to catch a deception and immediately make a new decision, which reflects reality instead of old programming. Truth sets you free!

Designed to Get to the Source

The Kalos Process was designed to get to the source of a problem by linking a condition or behavior to the original thought or subconscious decision. It is not a "fix it" or problem solving process to find an answer to each problem; instead it is designed to bring people to the core belief underlying many problems. Rather than only working at a conscious "positive thinking" level, the Process was designed to change attitudes that arise from a subconscious level. Through the use of MRT you are now able to communicate to that deep level of programming and investigate what is there!

Most dysfunctional behavior stems from decisions that are made at a very young age, even before a child is aware of those decisions. Your attitude stems from years of mental patterns based upon true or false beliefs about yourself and others. The intention of the Process is to be able to fulfill the scriptural advice to:

"Be transformed by the renewing of your mind."

Renewing your mind is the process of replacing false beliefs with new information that promotes loving resolution to life's questions, allowing you the magical ability to live "in the Spirit," "by the Spirit" and "for the Spirit." It is a way of expressing from your heart what your head (mind) wants in order to live. Old judgmental programming and dogmas get in the way of "seeing" clearly. They block the truth; therefore, you automatically re-act, instead of acting according to the highest love and wisdom within you. Because of repressed emotions based upon false beliefs, little annoyances become huge upsets that lead to emotional and physical ailments. Rarely are those present time upsets about what is happening today. They are unresolved shadows of the past coming back to be healed!

You Are in Charge of Your Own Process

The person going through The Process is always in charge. The assistant, called a Facilitator, supports and reports, but does not lead. <u>No advice is given during a Process</u>. All information comes from the individual, so the Facilitator does not need to be a trained psychologist or therapist. You can learn to guide yourself through The Process and clear a present time problem, whose roots are in the past.

The Process may appear to be a memorized structure, but it is not. Using it as a structure hampers the results. You will soon gain a feel for the movement of The Process, as well as an intuitive sense, which helps guide you to the next step.

The Kalos Process is based upon PRINCIPLES. The principles of living in harmony with life and functioning out of WHO we are as loving, <u>non-judgmental spiritual beings</u>. Many have said to me that they experienced unconditional love for the very first time during The Process. Harmonious relationships can replace old scars of resentment and shame. Through The Kalos Process you can take charge of your mind, instead of being a victim of its false assumptions and beliefs, or a slave to its hidden agenda. You are not your programming! You are the one in charge of it!

Patterns of Behavior Are Exposed

Noticing HOW you feel WHEN you're feeling it opens your awareness. Then you can explore what is going on in the inner realms of the mind. Through The Process, you will uncover hidden thoughts and feelings that have developed into attitudes of behavior. Your thoughts and feelings can be divided. You can <u>think</u> one way and <u>feel</u> another. This causes confusion to infiltrate your mind and cloud your thinking.

Major life issues can be resolved by exposing your unconscious beliefs that are driving your surface patterns of behavior. During The Process, you discover WHY your early programming comes up every time certain people or circumstances arise. Have you ever wondered how "grown-ups" can act so immaturely at times? Your hidden life patterns unveil before your eyes, as you get to know your little "child within." Most adult behavior is a result of early childhood programming based upon fear.

Gaining Understanding in the Kalos Process

It is your early childhood responses to people and situations that make up the bigger part of your individual mental and emotional patterns for life. You have an opportunity to look at these old patterns that no longer serve you, but were put there by a small child trying to handle an overwhelming world.

In the Kalos Process you experience looking at the other person's point of view through THEIR eyes, and experiencing their experience of life with a "double aware-ness." Seeing the *truth* of the matter brings understanding that creates the necessary compassion to allow healing to take place. Many times what we have judged to be an-other's motivation, is not true. Healing can result through the process of understanding. You will usually find that people did NOT know what was right and do wrong any-way. They really did have a positive intention.

By actually walking in another's shoes, you think their thoughts and feel their feelings. When you see "their truth" from this perspective, you can heal your own mis-judgments and resolve your misconceptions. Compassion and forgiveness heal deep wounds. You will discover that most of the time *there is nothing to forgive*. You get to experience the "love that surpasses understanding" — like being born anew!

Others Can Be Affected by Your Process

Amazingly, many people have reported how the pro-cessing they did actually affected another person, often one with whom they had an issue, who was not even present during The Process. Moreover, sometimes when healing your own mental/emotional patterns, others in your family with the same patterns can be affected by The Process. One lady said that when she healed her food addictions, two of her brothers stopped their compulsive drinking!

Your influence can extend beyond your body's bound-aries and reach out in some miraculous way, touching the lives of others, even from a distance. Remember the last time when you were thinking of someone and sure enough, just then, they called you on the phone? What is this, that reaches out and touches others unaware? We are just beginning to scratch the surface of our extraordinary, expansive dimensions.

Your family members likely have many of the same patterns as you have. It was probably no accident that you were born into that particular family with those particular patterns. Maybe, you actually CHOSE that mother and father! What would be the benefit of that?

Compassion and Understanding

You can observe your mind in a unique way when going back in time and replaying the old tapes during The Process. Only this time, you can get in touch with all of the hidden feelings that were going on and SPEAK OUT what you have kept suppressed! You can finally say the things that were so hard to say then! This time, you are able to see with added vision and speak the truth, even though it may be uncomfortable. Speaking out your feelings creates the space for new information to fill its place. Once there is space within the mind to discover new truths, you can then open up to why that person acted the way they did. Compassion and understanding are a result of seeing "what is so!"

The extraordinary experience is when
you realize there is nothing more to forgive!

Feeling unloved or that someone wants to hurt you causes faulty programming, because it is not true! Even if your parents wanted to not love you, they couldn't. People who are parents can truly answer this next question: Can you stop loving your child right now? Of course you can't; love is the very essence of your being! You are love! It is practically all you can do! You were created in the image of God, who is Love!

In a Process most people discover they really were loved. It is just that the love was expressed in a very immature way. That parent or person involved was doing the best he or she could do under the circumstances and with their own programming. Our first model of love, our parents, brought with them all their immature programming from their youth. When you see how far back some of the patterns go, you realize that your parents were doing the best they could at the time. What a wonderful experience to discover why a person acted in a certain way. Discovering how much you were loved is a very healing part of the process. Some have cried at the end of The Process saying, "That is the first time I felt my mother loved me." The more you feel that someone really didn't love you, the bigger the breakthrough when the truth is known. Resistance to "seeing the truth" can hamper The Process. This happens when you would rather be right about your not being loved, than be healed or be happy.

For generations man has lived with survival as the main motivation in life. Still the survival mechanism pushes people to their limits. On a physical level, survival works very well. On an emotional level, it gets in the way of happy harmonious relationships and serving our fellow man. Not long ago, simple tasks like bringing in the water or chopping wood were a matter of survival. Is it any wonder why people make simple acts so important?

The purpose of the Kalos Process is for healing to take place in the physical body and in the mental/emotional state by getting to the cause. When you let go of destructive patterns and emotions, including feelings of being a victim, the immune system is turned on and allows healing to take place. The body's immune system, if given the chance, is powerful enough to destroy anything that might attack.

Maturing your mind gives your immune system that chance. When you mature the mental programming, you identify the cluster of emotions (immature ego state) that is keeping you stuck in the old belief pattern and transform it into a new image that supports your full potential now.

Maturing up the Old Programming

Most of the time, as soon as you see the *truth* in a Process, your mind automatically changes (renews). Your thoughts and feelings transform into new mature programming that supports the healing process. You then understand WHY that person acted in a specific manner. Understanding their *positive intent* allows the truth to be seen. The positive intent is how they *think* they are correct and *feel* right, proper, or justified in their behavior. It may be difficult to imagine that every act has a positive intent behind it, so don't believe it! Just be open to the possibility of it.

225

One way to see this possibility is to think back on your own life when you behaved wrongly and ask yourself what you were thinking at the exact time of the behavior. Are you open to the possibility that before you said or did something, in that moment you felt it was right, proper or justified? Check it out! You may have changed your feelings moments later by realizing that what you did was NOT right, proper or justified, though in the exact moment of action, you felt it was. Just think, <u>every act may have a positive motive</u>, no matter how immature or hurtful the behavior might be! Understanding this supports you to love unconditionally, to have compassion and make allowances for your own misgivings. You may find that to the degree that you love and understand yourself, you can love and understand others.

You Are in Charge of Your World

When you see the benefit of your choices, you begin to break your pattern of being a victim. When you imagine that you can CREATE YOUR WORLD, it opens and releases new energy in your life, allowing you to experience being IN CHARGE! A new joy unfolds. A new gratitude expresses itself. You get to DISCOVER your own mind and your own ability to be in charge. The truth (what's really so) still sets you free. A Divine connection is realized as A HEALING MODE BEGINS. (A healing mode means that the body/mind is doing all it can do to bring balance, healing and normal function.)

Healing Energy Releases During The Process

Healing energy is released when you unleash your ability to feel love and gratitude. For example, when you are doing something you love to do, you have an endless amount of energy. In this same manner, your body supports you most when you are happy and filled with appreciation. Appreciation is the most healing energy the body can experience on a feeling level. Therefore, the design of The Kalos Process is to do more than heal unwanted emotional blocks. <u>It is to reprogram correct, positive information into the circuits of the body, so appreciation can flourish.</u>

Being transformed requires becoming transparent. That means that you are willing to tell the truth about your thoughts and feelings; knowing and feeling the *truth*, to be set free.

The next Chapter takes you through the various Steps of The Process. You will have an opportunity to practice processing with a project of your own by writing it down or by having a partner to work with you. Please study the Ethical Guidelines well and be open for the miracle of healing to transpire!

ETHICAL AND PROFESSIONAL GUIDELINES

For Utilizing The Kalos Process and Methodologies

PLEASE:

- Be participant-centered by being fully present to the participant's experience in a non-judgmental way.
- Facilitate them to breakthrough and be empowered by **their own** Process. The participant leads, the facilitator follows.
- Be respectful. Do not argue with a participant or challenge their beliefs or contradict their experience with how you might have felt if you had been there, etc.
- Encourage the participant. Do not push them to a breakthrough or badger them to let go or pull them out of a feeling. Encourage them to *feel their feelings* and let their heart speak.
- Be empathetic and objective. Deeply connect with the participant in their experience. Remain objective so that you don't get caught up in their story. Separate yourself from their issues and remain effective in the process. Identify with their experience and yet be detached. Look for the benefit in their experience. It assists you to be detached.
- Let them know they are doing well and support them wherever they are in their ability to express. There is no *right* way to feel. It is not *wrong* to *think* your feelings.

- Do not relate situations back to you, "That sounds like something that happened to me..." Don't talk about yourself.
- Do not give advice, spiritual counsel or intuitive insights, unless credentialed to do so. Then do it outside of a Kalos Process. Kalos is about the participant's insights, not advice.
- Do not recommend any medical treatments: colonics, mineral baths, fasts. Allow *their* body to tell them through MRT.
- Do not prescribe specific remedies such as: herbal, homeopathic, tinctures or any type of medicine. Let *their* body tell *them* what they need through MRT.
- Do not offer any vitamins, minerals or supplements.
- Do not share contents of The Process with others. Keep confidentiality.
- Do not share with a third party unless they are being asked to contribute to improve your ability or the participant's experience. Then do not mention any specific names or their circumstances without written permission.
- Dress tastefully and use neutral or gentle colors for accurate MRT.
- No flirtations or sexual involvements with participants/ clients. Be respectful and courteous, thoughtful and sincere.
- Do not criticize or condemn, gripe or speak negatively of someone who is not present. No gossiping.

Remember, The *Kalos Process* is not:

A treatment of any physical, mental, or emotional illness.

A substitute for ongoing therapy (medical or psychological).
About giving advice on how to solve the problems of life.
About taking sides or establishing blame.
About deciding what is right or wrong.
A magic pill that guarantees a non-disturbed state.

Be the Space of Transformation

Commit to the participant's reaching his/her goal. Make sure each Process is complete with understanding the past and having a clear picture for future results.
Support everyone to heal the cause, no matter what background, culture or religion. All can be supported.
Stand for each person being empowered.
Stand for the ongoing event of healing by following up with an ongoing plan for completion in any area.
Detach from the result and trust in the miracle of healing.

Highlights

- The Kalos Process, developed from the Relaxed Focused Attention (RFA) Process, was created to support people to transform their lives and realize their spiritual goals through achieving a perpetual positive attitude that glorified God.

- Our attitude is the biggest factor in our health and stems from decisions that were made at a very young age.

- The Kalos Process was designed to wake up our consciousness to "see the truth" of the matter and stop us from going into old fear-based programming.

- The Kalos Process reveals the initial cause of problems by going to when the problem began and exposing the deception involved.

- The intention of The Process is to "Transform your life by the renewing of your mind," which is the process of replacing false beliefs with new information that promotes loving resolution.

- You are in charge of your own Process. A Facilitator supports you to heal yourself.

- No advice is given during a Process.

- The Process is based upon principles of living in harmony with life and functioning out of a non-judgmental state.

- Major life issues can be resolved by exposing your unconscious beliefs that are driving you.

- Compassion and forgiveness heals deep wounds. You get to gain a "love that surpasses understanding" — like being born anew!

- Speaking out suppressed emotions creates the space for compassion and understanding to fill its place.

- The extraordinary experience is when you realize there is nothing more to forgive!

- As the *truth* is seen in a Process, your mind matures itself.

- A *positive intent* is always at the core of a behavior. Understanding it allows the truth to be seen.

- Understanding the *positive intent* behind any action is to understand that before anyone can do or say anything, in that moment they must *feel* it is right, proper or justified, or they can't do it!

- When you see the benefit of your choices, you begin to break the pattern of being a victim. Imagine that you create your world!

- Being transformed requires becoming transparent. That means that you are willing to tell the truth about your thoughts and feelings. Knowing and feeling the *truth* can "set you free!"

Chapter Twelve

Pretesting and Open Eyed Processing

Pretesting prepares the way to understanding the **cause** by revealing what needs aligning mentally and emotionally. The following Chapter walks you through the steps of The Kalos Process. You can find the exact age of the onset of the problem and set the stage for understanding the cause. Identifying the plot characters and the emotions involved give clues to resolution. It is part of the research into who, where, when, and why that any good researcher needs. Accessing this information through Muscle Response Testing (MRT) informs the mind that there is something more to understand.

As you walk through The Kalos Process, you will notice how it can be used beyond a structured process. The principles of honesty, understanding and truth can work as a guide for problems in everyday life. The methods of The Process are useful in handling the upsetting detours your mind can take in normal living, giving you a way to process life's difficulties and prevent perpetrations from recurring. You can learn to stop, relax, rethink the situation and resolve the problem at hand.

Although there is only one *Kalos Process*, there are three major parts, each one uniquely taking on different characteristics. Each part can be used separately or in combination with another part. Pretesting and Open Eyed Processing are always used first, followed by either Closed Eyed Processing or Maturing of the Mind Processing or both, depending upon the circumstances. The most common sequence of The *Kalos Process* is:

1. Pretesting and Open Eyed Processing
2. Closed Eyed Processing
3. Maturing of the Mind Processing

The Process always begins with Pretesting and leads into Open Eyed Processing. The more information you can access in the beginning, the better. Many processes will be completed at this point because they get to the bottom of the matter quickly, simply by asking enough questions and answering them. Closed Eyed Processing is used at any time when emotions bubble up or when the problem began before memory. The Maturing of the Mind part of the processing is used when residual feelings are left after a Process or when added support is needed to give further guidance at accomplishing your goal through the use of Full Potential Advisors.

The more practiced you are in using the MRT techniques taught in Section II, the easier Pretesting will be. Much is dependent upon knowing:

1. How to do Muscle Response Testing (MRT).
2. How to do Trigger Point Emotional Testing.

3. How to do "Think/feel Testing."
4. How to do "Surrogate Testing" to test yourself.

Having a partner there with you, or knowing how to test yourself accurately is necessary to practice the following methods. Otherwise, I recommend that you withhold your practice until you are in a supportive environment with a Kalos Health Facilitator to assist you.

Hopefully, you will pick a simple project of your own and apply it to these methods as we go through them. Practice by writing each step (using your own project), as this will help you in making The Process more enjoyable and easier to learn.

Naming a Project - Identifying a Goal

What is missing that you want to have in your life, or what is happening that you do not like? Having a specific purpose or project for each Process is essential. To arrive at a result you must first <u>know where you want to go</u>. So, the first step is to find out **what you want** to improve the quality of your life, such as:

End a compulsion for _____ ;
Resolve a fear about changing careers, etc.;
Create a successful intimate relationship;
Heal a physical ache or pain;
Gain the freedom to _____ .

Be specific in your choice. Do not say, *"I want good health."* Your project should state exactly what you want accomplished to achieve good health; such as, *"I want to eliminate the excess weight that is causing pain in my knees."* Your project may be of a physical, emotional, or social nature. Many choose to process their physical problems first. Do this only when you have an experienced Health Facilitator to work with you. You will find it best to start with something simple to practice with, such as a relationship or a career project. Though focused on a single project, you will discover an underlying story for many areas of your life that need healing.

You can use your inner guidance or use MRT to test where to start. For example, you might say: *"The first thing I want to heal is my relationship with my father."* Then, test that statement. If the test is strong, it is a good choice. List all your possible projects. Be clear on where you are now with each project and where you want to go with it to achieve results. Often several projects are resolved in one Process, though your focus will be in only one area.

What you choose may also relate to whether you have someone there assisting you at this time. If you are by yourself reading this text, and do not know how to use MRT on yourself, pick a project that you can practice by writing it down. This would mean that you would use a personal habit you want to break or personal limitation that you want to expand.

To learn to do a Kalos Process successfully will require your practicing on someone else, and having him or her practice on you. This text is to give you the principles and steps in The Process, knowing that ultimately you will need hands-on guidance from someone trained in this work. Therefore, I will address each step as if you have a partner present to use for the testing. You can use a partner's arm to test yourself. This is called "Surrogate Testing," and is described in *Chapter Six*. I will write as if you were practicing on someone else called a partner. The following nine steps are used in all processing. You will want to memorize them.

1. Double Mind Testing, right and left brain alignment.
2. Age of Decision Testing, to locate onset of problem.
3. Dyslexia Testing at onset.
4. Emotional Point Testing at onset.
5. Testing who was involved and what was going on at the onset of the problem.
6. Speaking out feelings using Neuro-vascular Holding Points. Eyes are closed during this part.
7. Identifying the perpetration - Seeing the truth.
8. Seeing the benefit of the experience.
9. Retesting everything in alignment.

Open Eyed processing can bring resolution at any time during the testing and clearing. Sometimes during the first or second step a person will make a decision that changes their understanding. When a person sees who is involved and what is going on in Step Five, resolution can take place rapidly. Always make sure the emotions are cleared, if any come up. If there are strong emotions present in

Steps Four and Five, you may move right into Closed Eyed processing. You may also move into Closed Eyed processing if the problem's origin was before the age of conscious memory, i.e. age 5 and under. In this case you would still complete the Pretesting Steps through Number Five and go into the Closed Eyed processing described in the next Chapter.

I am cautious in presenting these Steps in such a linear way, as I do not want the methodology to interfere with using intuition in The Process. I also know that if you will memorize the Steps you will be more free to follow Spirit during The Process. You may find that you may complete a successful Process though not following the steps exactly and you may find The Process incomplete though following the steps exactly.

The Steps don't control The Process, they guide you through it. Your partner in The Process does the leading and is in charge of where The Process takes you. The flow of the Spirit will intuitively guide you, as you respond to your partner's answers. So please, like a musician memorizing the notes or learning the scales first, trust The Process to unfold itself through the Spirit. An abbreviated outline of the components of The Kalos Process is found at the end of *Chapter Sixteen*, following some sample Processes.

Pretesting

Once your partner's project (goal) is clear, you and your partner's Three Circuits are aligned by rubbing the clavicle bones, above and below the lips and over the tail bone, you are ready to do some pretesting. (Review *Chapter Six* for diagram and explanation.) Pretesting will give you information, which will help you in doing The Process quickly and efficiently. It tells you whether a person is single minded (thoughts and feelings aligned) about achieving their goal, the age capacity for achieving the goal, who is involved, and what emotions are present. Reread *Chapter Seven* for review of the THINK/FEEL DOUBLE MIND TESTING, if necessary, then continue.

A person may THINK one way and FEEL another about their project. Beginning with Double Mind Testing brings all resistances to the surface and identifies where you will focus for resolution to take place. The following steps will assist you:

1. **Double Mind Testing** (See *Chapter Ten*)
A. Determine if your partner is double or single minded about what he/she wants. Are their thoughts and feelings aligned to achieving their goal? Take this step first, so their mind will not be at odds with itself, resisting resolution during The Process. Record all statements that test weak. Have your partner repeat the following:

"I think I want . . ." (Add project, and you test)
"I feel I want . . ."
"I think I can . . ."
"I feel I can . . ."

The Double Mind Testing works as a gauge to let you know what is aligned and what is not.

Example:

> *"I think I want to come to my ideal weight."*
>   [MRT — Strong]
> *"I feel I want to come to my ideal weight."*
>   [MRT — Weak]
> *"I think I can come to my ideal weight."*
>   [MRT — Strong]
> *"I feel I can come to my ideal weight."*
>   [MRT — Weak]

Notice in the above example that both of the *thinking* parts were strong and both of the *feeling* parts were weak. Any part of the test may be weak or strong. This example indicates double mindedness; the conscious and subconscious mind are not aligned.

B. Ask and test each question, as it arises, to resolve the mind's conflict. Once your partner's goal is clear and you have completed Double Mind Testing, address each conflict by looking at all of the possibilities that could be getting in the way of achieving the goal. Ask:

"What is getting in the way?"

Use MRT for every answer, testing to see if that truly is the conflict. Remember, a strong test always means "yes" and a weak test always means "no." Keep feeding back questions from the answers until coming to single mindedness. This will let you know what is real to the mind and what is not. Examine the first weak test, as noted in the previous example.

Facilitator: *"What is getting in the way of your **feeling** you **want** to come to your ideal weight?"*

Partner: *"Maybe I don't want to do what it takes to get there - to exercise or starve myself."*

Facilitator: *"Repeat after me, I **feel** I do not want to exercise."*

Partner: *"I feel I do not want to exercise."* [MRT - Weak]

Facilitator: *"No, you actually do **not** have a problem with exercising. How do you feel about eating in a special way?"*

Partner: *"I **feel** deprived emotionally when I can't eat what I want."* [MRT - Strong]

Facilitator: *"Do you **think** you are deprived?"*

Partner: *"Yes, I **think** I am."* [MRT - Strong]

Facilitator: *"You have just arrived at the bottom line of your problem. You are actually single minded that you will be deprived. You have a belief that a special healthy diet plan would be depriving you of an important satisfying experience of eating anything you want. What is more satisfying of the two, your health and having your ideal weight, or your taste buds? It's your choice."*

Partner: *"My health first, and I want to feel better about myself by coming to my ideal weight."*

Notice how I fed back questions based upon the answers given. Always use their answer to give you your next question. She said that she might *feel deprived*. Therefore, I asked: *"Do you think that you would be deprived?"* Continue questions until coming to single mindedness.

For some people the above issue would be mostly resolved by simply understanding what was getting in the way of the goal of having one's ideal weight. This woman's health came up as one important issue to expand upon. If present time beliefs for health are strong enough, she could resolve this issue through an Open Eyed Process. Though, this issue could move into a Closed Eyed Process to uncover her age capacity to feel secure, instead of feeling deprived.

Understanding why a person has a particular goal is helpful in asking questions to uncover the cause. By going to the reason **why**, you speed up the process of achieving your goal. You can unblock deceptions at any part of The Process to achieving a goal. You simply would repeat the Double Mind Testing to get clear on that particular part of the plan, such as:

> *"I think I want to be healthy.*
> *I think I want to give myself a healthy body*
> *by eating correctly.*
> *I feel I do. I think I can. I feel I can."*

Almost always you will come to single mindedness during this part of The Process. Do not be concerned if you don't, as it will be resolved later during the emotional clearing or the Closed Eyed part of The Process. The more information you bring up with your questions, the faster The Process moves along. Many addictions can be overcome with only this Open Eyed part of The Process. I am continually astonished at the ability of the mind to support the new information and resolve problems fast.

If, in the beginning, all of the *think/feel* tests are strong, it means that your partner is already in the process of doing something about each issue. If this is the case, you then go to the next phase of achievement to support where they want to be. If originally all of the ideal weight tests were strong, the next phase would have been to set up a program to support single mindedness in the areas of: nutrition, exercise, a support group, etc., or wherever the need may be.

Example:

Facilitator: *"Since you are single minded about coming*
                 to your ideal weight, what is it that you need
                 to do to accomplish this?"

(Notice how all the answers are to come from the
person being tested.)

Partner: *"I think I need a good dietary plan."*
                 [MRT - Strong]
                 "I feel I need a good dietary plan."
                 [MRT - Strong]

Continue with *think/feel* testing for whether the person
can accomplish this task. Make sure that you support
them in setting up such a plan. Unless you are qualified to
give that particular type of counseling and they are asking
you to do so, only support them in their own decisions.
Questioning and testing can continue until all is testing
single minded or you can move to the next Step.

2.   Test Age of Decision[19] — Determine whether the
problem is of recent origin, or if it relates back to early
childhood by locating the <u>age</u> when the problem began.
Even though most symptoms do not appear until later, the
subconscious decision that created the problem may have

---

[19]The age when a decision is made or when a problem began with a
perpetration attached, having consequences of preventing further maturity in that area,
which can lead to emotional or physical consequences later.

happened earlier. Changes take place in the electrical field of your body before they become visible in the physical body. This was practiced in *Chapter Nine* under the discussion of dyslexia. The specific age at the beginning of the problem tells us the most important time to proceed with The Process. This is tested by stating an age into the body circuitry using MRT, as follows:

State, ___(The problem)___ began at age 30 or younger (test), age 20 or younger (test), etc. When the arm goes weak, you then state the next older age until the test is strong again. This will give you the exact age.

As an example:

"Having my ideal weight began to be a problem at age 30 or younger, [MRT — Strong]
    age 20 or younger,   [MRT — Strong]
    age 10 or younger,   [MRT — Weak]
A weak test means to go higher in age.
    age 12 or younger,   [MRT — Weak]
    age 15 or younger,   [MRT — Strong]
    age 14 or younger,   [MRT — Strong]
    age 13 or younger,"   [MRT — Weak]

Remember, a strong test always means YES, while a weak test always means NO. This is the reason that a question is always formulated in a positive way to support this premise. Can you see how the correct age in this situation is 14? You find the age by going to where the strong test is the closest to the weak test. You can begin the testing at any age. In most situations people know around the time that the problem began, so you don't have to use so many ages. Now that you have used MRT to substantiate the exact age or time of decision, state the exact age in the circuit by saying,

> a. *"Age fourteen in the circuit."* (Use MRT)
> > Then go to the next test.
> b. *"Circuits in the clear."* (Use MRT)
> > This is to make sure that placing that age
> > in the body circuitry didn't cause a short
> > circuit. If weak, correct the circuits.

NOTE: *Any time you get a weak test, retest the muscle to make sure it is strong before you do another test. This allows the muscle to re-energize before the next test.*

These two tests make sure that the proper age is in the circuit and that the three electrical circuits are in balance at that age, so you can accurately test for the remaining information.

3. Dyslexia Testing (see *Chapter Nine*) — Especially when working with a problem relating to dyslexia or a learning disability, I recommend that you check to see if a *dyslexic* condition was present at the age of decision. To do this, have the person look at an "X" and the "railroad tracks," using MRT. If the "X" tests weak, it means that whatever happened caused a "switching off" of one side of the brain from the other. Emotional dyslexia is very common at every "Age of decision" in almost every problem. This tells you that the experience had deeply felt reactions and that the Brain Integration Exercises will be helpful as a follow-up.

In the above example with a weight problem, the lady would use the statement: "I love being my ideal weight" for her Brain Integration Exercise. These exercises can help you in any area of your life that you want to change a belief or attitude. The humming and rolling your eyes in a circle embeds the statement into a subconscious level of memory. Remember to support a person to feel love and compassion for himself and others during a Process. The lack of loving support is the basis of most people's problems, especially dyslexia. Be certain to <u>retest the "X" after using The Kalos Process</u>. You will find this to be another great barometer to gauge your accomplishments, plus to seal the subconscious programming in a positive way.

4. Emotional Point Testing (*Chapter Eight*) — Test Emotional "trigger points" with the proper age in the circuit. Using your index finger (or all your fingers) and focusing on the emotion being tested, lightly touch each point while doing a muscle response test and record them. Remember to always keep neutral and approach each point with the thought, "This is strong or balanced." The MRT will let you know what is out of balance.

247

Knowing the emotions involved in the problem speeds up the process of surfacing the exact experience that got programmed inaccurately. Bringing the long-held emotions to the surface gives you an opportunity to get to the perpetration (deception) behind them. Testing these points is a useful yardstick to see what emotions have been released from a subconscious level during The Process.

As an example, the lady with the weight problem had several Emotion Points test weak: frustration, overwhelmed burden, suppressed anger, resentment/control, and need for approval. Testing these points and bringing the old memory of these feelings to the surface made it easier for her to recall what happened.

If a student begins crying or showing signs of emotional overwhelm during the testing of these points, hold their forehead, as described in "Step 6." to release those emotions from a subconscious level. Always retest the Emotion Points after The Process is finished to make sure all are cleared. Any remaining emotions indicate that The Process is not completed. This "post testing" allows you to check your work and places a seal of permanency upon the mind's programming.

5. Test <u>Who</u> Was Involved and <u>What</u> Was Going On — After uncovering the emotions present at that age, you can then find out WHO was involved and WHAT was going on. When the age goes before memory, Closed Eyed processing is needed, as described in the next Chapter. You will want to be very familiar with the next Chapter, of course, before doing any processing for the first time. This way you will know how to move into a Closed Eyed Process from here.

Make sure that the age of the test is still "in the circuit" because moving around during The Process can remove the statement out of the circuit. Restate, "Age _____ in the circuit," as taught in Step 2, and have the person think of each possible person who might be involved in his life at that time and muscle test. Anyone who tests weak is involved with the problem. Usually only a few people are involved, such as: mom, dad, brothers, sisters, grandparents, guardian, friends, a baby sitter, a teacher, mate, ex-mate, etc. When the people are identified, the mind will usually come up with an experience to confirm what happened that caused the upsetting emotions tested earlier. Now, using MRT, you can connect all the missing pieces. Using the weight problem, I offer the following example:

a. "Age fourteen in the circuit." (Use MRT)
b. "Circuits in the clear." (Strong test means yes, weak test means to correct the circuits.)
c. Say, "Think of Mom." (Student thinks of Mom) Use MRT. (Repeat this process until all possible people have been tested.)
d. Test what circumstance might be involved by stating:

"This problem happened at home." (MRT)
"This problem happened at school." (MRT)
"This problem had to do with being assaulted." (MRT), etc.

249

Use MRT to validate each statement. Do not ask the body questions, such as, "Did this problem happen at home?" Make a clear statement and then use MRT, remembering that a strong test always means "yes" and a weak test always means "no."

When someone discovers who and what was involved, they usually begin the healing process. Do not rush through this Open Eyed component of The Process, as not only does healing begin to resolve the problem, but also this may be the only part needed for completion.

Once, when I was testing a lady with a tumor in her uterus, I found that it had begun to appear at an electrical unconscious level seven years earlier, when she divorced her husband. Of course, she never knew what was happening inside her body from the deep emotional loss. She was carrying her ex-husband around in her uterus, which was clustered with debilitating emotions. This knowledge, gained from pretesting, initiated her healing process. Two people in the class began to smell a strange odor and saw vapors leave her body. Weeks later, she reported the tumor was gone. It is no surprise that the tumor formed there. Having problems in the sexual organs that relate to a present time or former mate is very common. A similar story of a woman with a cyst in her uterus is mentioned in Book One, *A New Day In Healing, Chapter Three.*

Emotions will block energy in the body wherever the body is affected the most; such as, when one feels like crying, emotions get blocked in the eyes, head and throat. When you feel sorry for yourself, your sinuses will get stuffy, etc. When you tense up with resentment, look for arthritis in those tense joints and formerly injured areas.

You can find trapped emotions almost everywhere the body is affected by inflammation and/or growths.

If you want to explore this further, find out which emotions are weak and what area of the body tests weak. By identifying both the weak emotions and a weak area of the body, you can then touch both points at the same time and do MRT. Two weak areas equal a strong test if they are connected. This testing will tell you which specific emotions are trapped in any area of the body.

Trigger Point Testing any weak area while touching an Emotional Point will determine whether those two areas are connected. A strong test indicates that there is a connection. A weak test indicates there is not.

Encourage your partner to allow their emotions to come up to the surface and share them, or write them down. Also encourage your partner to share any stories that come up from the past in relation to their project. When emotions become visible during the pretesting, or any time during The Process, hold the Neuro-vascular Holding Points over their forehead, as described below. The Neuro-vascular Holding Points can support one to release those emotions from a subconscious level.

6. Speaking out Emotions Using the Neuro-vascular Holding Points (See *Chapter Eight*) — When emotions surface during any part of The Process, holding the Neuro-vascular Holding Points on the forehead will release those emotions from a subconscious level.

Encourage your partner to feel their feelings and notice where those feelings are in their body. Notice who is involved in the upset and SPEAK OUT THOSE FEEL-INGS directly to the people involved. This starts the diffusing process that "creates space," exposes what has triggered the insecurity or fear, and stimulates compassion and understanding.

Sometimes, I will make a trail back to the first time by using several incidents along the way to create more space. If anytime you sense going to another age would be valuable, follow your inner guidance and go there! Stay so close to your partner in The Process that it becomes your process too. You, as the Facilitator, can gain much while supporting your partner to heal. Don't worry about your own tears that might come up, while supporting your partner to heal. Just feel your feelings and be there totally. There are many ways to make The Process work. I am more interested in results, than I am in reasons for doing The Process in a particular way.

Fully support your partner by reminding them: "Re-experiencing your past with the same feelings and perspective, only with a new ability to SPEAK OUT old hurts because you are older and wiser now, releases the pent-up emotions that have been blocking physical and emotional healing. When the situation happened, you may have been too afraid, confused, and unsure of your feelings to express them fully.

Holding the palm of your hand over the back of their head helps them access past time information *(Chapter Eight)*. This, along with holding their forehead, is enough to find and release all the vital information to support their clearing.

The pretesting prepares the way for healing to take place by going to the exact time of the onset of the problem. It sets the stage by identifying the plot characters and the emotions involved. Clues to resolution are then uncovered. It is part of the research that goes into who, when, where, and why that any good detective needs. Accessing this information may have a humbling effect upon the mind, as it lets go of premature judgments and blame.

7. Finding the Perpetration — See the Truth — The Process focuses on "Understanding the truth to be set free." If you are willing to experiment, you will find, as I have, that every negative emotion is connected to a perpetration. When you truly know the REALITY in life, you want to celebrate! You want to rejoice in the love and beauty that are here. You will find that most suffering comes from deceptions, stories that you believe to be true, that are not. Staying in your "story" placed there by a doubtful, fearful mind can bring discouragement, sickness and premature death.

As you keep asking questions from previous answers, you will always uncover duality and deception. This information can be proven though MRT. Keep testing until the TRUTH is known.

8. See the Benefit of the Experience — Often this is the final part necessary to resolve the problem. Completing The Process here indicates that the truth has been revealed and that your partner is now free from being driven by the perpetration in their mind. It means that they have discovered that they really are good enough or loved enough, etc. Seeing how their life has benefited from their earlier decision brings a kind of grace to the healing process. No matter how much they have strived to overcome its effects, the compensation has brought benefits. When The Process ends here, it is an indication that the problem began after the age of conscious memory and therefore an OPEN EYED PROCESS is sufficient.

9. **Retest** all Emotion Points and Think/Feel statements to make sure all are strong and the body is aligned in its project or goal. Whether The Process is finished here or whether you go on to complete it in the next Chapter, the mind is just like a computer that can change data and affect all the other parts; the mind can "rethink" a situation by seeing new truth about it. It is fascinating to see how through re-experiencing a past incident with present time perception, a person can change the effect of it on their life now.

Although you will always use the Open Eyed part of The Process, much of the time you will be using the Closed Eyed part also. I consistently use the Open Eyed Process for overcoming addictions, present time fears, career changes, and just becoming single minded in purpose. It is common to begin with Open Eyed Processing and end up in Closed Eyed Processing as the problem gets traced back to its earliest time before conscious memory. As you practice the steps in this Chapter, you can easily add the steps in the next. See *Chapter Thirteen* for example Processes. I suggest that you go to a free introductory lecture in your area to see a demonstration and to practice your skills.

Highlights

- Pretesting prepares the way by revealing what subconscious programming needs aligning, as well as uncovering who is involved, your age of decision, what emotions were present, etc.

- You can use The Kalos Process in your daily life. You can learn to stop, relax, rethink the situation and resolve the problem at hand.

- There is only one Kalos Process, although it has three major components — Open Eyed, Closed Eyed and Maturing of the Mind Processing.

- The Process begins with pretesting and leads into Open Eyed Processing.

- Choose a project (goal) to apply the methods learned here in a specific way: What do you want to happen in your life, or what do you want to stop happening for your life to be successful?

- You can test yourself through Surrogate Testing. This is how you can also test babies or invalids.

- Double Mind Testing lets you know if you are aligned in how you **think** and **feel** about what you want.

After each statement use MRT:

"I think I want . . ." (add your project)
"I feel I want . . ."
"I think I can . . ."
"I feel I can . . ."

● Test the Age of Decision when the problem began.

"Age 30 or younger,
Age 20 or younger, etc." Keep going until the test
goes weak. Then back up to the first strong year
after the weak test.

● Problems begin in the electrical body first; therefore,
you can find a problem before it becomes manifested
in physical form. MRT makes a wonderful prevention tool.

● Dyslexia testing lets you know if one hemisphere of
the brain has switched off during an upset. If it has,
use the Brain Integration Exercises after The Process.

● Testing the Emotion Points will identify what emotions
are involved with the problem and helps surface the
upset. Testing emotions also function as a barometer
for when The Process is completed.

● Test who was involved and what was going on. Exposing the truth supports the healing process.

- Allow your emotions to surface and share them through speaking them out loud, holding the Neuro-vascular Holding Points over the forehead.

- The Neuro-vascular Holding Points can be used any-time you have an upset and need to release stress in or out of a Process.

- The Kalos Process focuses on "Understanding the truth to be set free," and transforming old responses through understanding the benefit of what happened.

  Every negative emotion is connected to a perpetration. When the truth is known, the suffering disappears.

- Open Eyed Processing is used for addictions, fears, career changes, and just becoming single minded in any area of your life. Every Process begins with it.

Chapter Thirteen

The Kalos
Closed Eyed Process

Even though many problems are resolved with the Open Eyed part of The Process, many times a deeper level of awareness and understanding is required. The Closed Eyed part of The Process is added when any of the following is present:

a. The original situation or problem goes before memory.
b. Insight is needed requiring looking through another person's eyes to gain an understanding of the behavior.
c. Unresolved emotions need clearing.
d. "Generational healing" is desired to heal family patterns.

Before you begin, please be aware that I am not recommending that you go through this Closed Eyed part of The Process alone until you know the steps well and have had experience with others. I recommend that you have a Kalos Health Facilitator or other trained professional present to practice the following steps.

With the pre-testing information in hand, you enter the second phase of The Process fully ready and aware of the major issues. So get comfortable and relax! You will want to memorize the following **Seven Steps** to facilitate your partner's Process:

1. **Partner sits or lies down, closes eyes and relaxes**.
2. **Go to the time when the problem began.**
3. **Identify *feelings* about what happened and Speak out trapped emotions.**
4. **Walk in another person's shoes and see their point of view.**
5. **Find the perpetration.**
6. **Release compassion, understanding & forgiveness.**
7. **See the benefit.**

1. Student sits in a chair or lies down, whatever is most comfortable, closes eyes and relaxes. Just taking a couple of slow, deep breaths to relax is sufficient to begin focusing attention on inner feelings. Focusing in a relaxed state is what meditation is all about. Many peak experiences in my life have been experienced in this state. Many call this an "alpha state" of awareness, a type of focused state that is often experienced unconsciously, while watching a movie.

While your partner is in this relaxed state, place your hands over his or her frontal eminence bones on the forehead, as described in *Chapter Eight,* p. 159, under: Neuro-vascular Holding Points. The technique of holding the Neuro-vascular Points on the forehead will facilitate releasing stressful emotions from a subconscious level during The Process.

2. Go to the time when the problem began. In the Open Eyed part of The Process, MRT was used to find the first time the problem occurred; now you will <u>go to that age</u> and get in touch with what went on. This is where the Closed Eyed part of The Process overlaps the Open Eyed part of The Process.

Remind your partner to keep his/her experience as if it were in the present time. Since our "right brain" stores information in the form of feelings and pictures, encourage your partner to look at what is going on as a "NOW" experience in order to feel his/her feelings. Encourage transparency and telling the truth about thoughts and feelings.

Since the purpose of The Kalos Process is to get to the CAUSE of the problem, you <u>always</u> go to the <u>first time</u> the problem occurred (Age of Decision). Then, you can find out who was initially involved and what emotions were present. This is similar to the use of a "night scope" which reveals the terrain in the dark. You are then able to better plan your strategy. <u>Look at WHAT is going on and WHO is involved.</u> Have your partner relate all the information that comes up. If their eyes open any time during The Process, simply request that they close them again and stay focused.

Knowing who and what is involved at the onset of the problem can aid in understanding the reaction to the situation. It was the suppressed anger and held resentment of the woman with the tumor that caused the tumor to form, not the outward circumstances. She had never told her husband how she felt! She suppressed her thoughts and feelings, pretending they did not exist! She created a perpetration (lie) around not being able to speak out her feelings, because she <u>believed</u> women had to do as they were told and not question their husband's actions. She gave away her personal choice! You could say that giving up choice is like giving away your personal power, your LIFE!

3. Identify *feelings* **about what happened and Speak out trapped emotions** (This is also described in *Chapter Twelve*, Step 6.) Identifying feelings, noticing where they are felt in the body, then speaking them out as if it were the time of the experience, will create the space for the *truth* to show up. Only as you get the emotional blocks out of the way can you make room for new programming. The student can re-experience from that same perspective and with the same feelings as in the past, only with a new ability to SPEAK OUT old hurts, because at the time when the situation happened they were too afraid, confused, and unsure of their feelings. Make sure that you identify all of the feelings held inside. Look for one that all the others cluster around, such as feeling trapped, rejected, confused, etc. (Later, when you are more practiced in The Process, you may want to take a major emotion back to an earlier time and even to a generational pattern in a parent or grandparent.)

Speaking out, while holding the points on the forehead releases held emotions and *creates space* for the truth to be seen and understood. When you are cluttered with emotions, opinions and beliefs about a situation, you are not open to discovering the truth about it. The mind would rather be correct (about its misconceptions) than be happy.

The woman with the tumor in her uterus had known about her problem for only a year; therefore, could not go to the real cause. She could identify frustrations at that time, but none that really had any relationship to her former husband. She had to go to the time when the tumor began to grow to identify what was going on that triggered her condition. The pre-testing established her age at the onset, as well as who was involved and all of the feelings that were judged and suppressed. The tumor took several years to develop and then to be discovered in the physical realm, but the repressed emotions were hiding out in her uterus all that time from the age of onset.

Encourage the person to feel their feelings and notice where those feelings are in their body. Identify as many feelings as possible. Notice who is involved in the upset and SPEAK OUT THOSE FEELINGS. This starts the diffusing process that *creates space*, exposes what has triggered the insecurity or fear, and stimulates compassion and understanding. Once there is space within the mind by speaking out repressed feelings, you can then open up to understand why that person acted that way. In the next step you will get to discover why they acted the way they did and what their positive intent was for doing so.

4. Walking in another person's shoes and seeing their viewpoint aids in discovering the truth that can set you free of the perpetration. Understanding is reached when you can see and feel what they were experiencing at the time of your upset. Before your partner walks into another person's shoes always ask, "<u>Do you understand why that person acted that way</u>?" This prompts the mind to want to know why! The mind will always want to be polite, even though looking at another's viewpoint can be very intimidating for fear of being wrong or not being loved.

Sometimes a partner will say, "Yes, I understand why." Let them tell you and ask again, "Do you understand the purpose behind that?" Keep asking them what is behind each reason they give until they say, "I don't know." Then you can say, "Would you like to understand why?" The inquisitive mind always wants to know why! Therefore, you will receive all the inner support to get to the bottom line of the problem.

During The Process your partner can observe past experiences in a unique way. He or she can go back in time, replay the old tapes and look at the situation from another person's viewpoint. The other person's feelings can be experienced and their positive intent behind those actions can be understood. This time, they are able to observe the situation inside out and backwards, and with the added knowledge of later experiences.

Feeling unloved or that someone wants to hurt you can cause faulty programming. By going into the other person's head, you get to see their viewpoint and feel what they felt. People get to discover they really were loved, only the love was expressed in an immature way. That person was doing the best they could do under the circumstances and with the programming they had from childhood.

It is a wonderful experience to discover why the other person acted the way they did. To discover how much you were loved is a very healing part of The Process. Some have cried at the end of The Process saying, "That is the first time I felt my mother loved me." The more you feel someone doesn't love you, the bigger the breakthrough when the truth is known.

Our first model of love, our parents, brought with them all their immature programming from their youth. When you see how far back some of the patterns go, you see how much that survival has been the primary motivator in the generations of the past. Even now, the survival mechanism pushes people to their limits. On a physical level, it works very well. On an emotional level, it gets in the way of happy, harmonious relationships. Just simple tasks, like bringing in the water or chopping wood, not long ago were a matter of survival. Is it any wonder why people make simple acts so important?

Example: **"Walking in another person's shoes."**

Facilitator: "Now that you have expressed your feelings and have asked for what you want, do you understand why that person (Dad) acted that way?"

Partner:	"No," is the usual answer. (If the student says, "yes," ask them to tell you the reason. Then ask them if they understand <u>why</u> they did <u>that</u>! Keep going until they finally say, "No, I don't understand." (Always come to a place where the mind does not know, so it will be open to learn.)

Facilitator:	"Would you like to understand why?"
Partner:	"Yes."

Facilitator:	"You won't take anything out that can hurt you in any way." (This statement is to place your partner at ease before moving into the other person's head and looking through their eyes. There may be resistance when going into a person's head who has done a violent act. Of course, they cannot take anything out that can hurt them, anyway.)

Partner may not say anything at this time. This is fine. With resistance, use patience. Then, move along with their permission; never argue or force the issue.

Facilitator:	"Look at the person (Dad) in front of you; now, you go around to the back of Dad and look at the back of Dad's head; now walk up right next to his head. Now move right inside his head and look through his eyes and you feel his feelings. What are you

> feeling? Are they happy or sad? Speak out
> your feelings. Speak as if you are Dad, not
> yourself in Dad, by saying 'I feel . . ..'"

Notice all of the feelings and take them back to
when they began and speak them out. Identify the decision
that caused the reaction. You often will find yourself
repeating the first part of The Process having to do with
identifying an earlier episode that created a similar reaction. Make sure the person's behavior is understood.
Understanding **why** they acted the way they did supports
the student in The Process of identifying the perpetration,
what they thought was true, but was not. Identifying the
perpetration is the key to understanding the truth to be "set
free." Often you will discover that forgiveness comes
naturally or is not necessary, because you understand why
the person acted that way.

5. Release compassion, understanding & forgiveness -
After you identify when, where and who was involved in
the earlier episode, give loving compassion to yourself at
that age. Remember that you were doing the best you
could at the moment. Use all of your senses to do this.
Make it real! When you express compassion for yourself,
it opens the door to also having compassion for the others
involved.

By lovingly understanding and forgiving yourself
you make it much easier to forgive someone else. This is
an important part to remember in The Process, as love is
the greatest healer. Do not hide, deny or diminish your
feelings, but experience them fully, allowing them to be

felt, seen and heard so that they might be healed. Compassion will be the result!

6. Find the perpetration - Going to the first time of the problem, exposes the hidden belief that has crept into the mind because of fear. You don't realize that false beliefs are buried there. You can discover their existence when you keep trying to accomplish something that doesn't happen. When struggle in an area of your life is the norm, there is usually a perpetration present. As stated earlier, a perpetration is a hidden belief you hold about yourself that is not true, but deceives you into a negative reaction, like self doubt or fear.

The purpose of The Kalos Process is for healing to take place by exposing the cause. When you let go of destructive beliefs and emotions, including feelings of being a victim, you turn on your immune system and allow healing to take place. The body's immune system is powerful enough to destroy anything that might attack you, if given the chance.

Example: **Finding the perpetration**

Facilitator: "Now that you have looked at the situation through the other person's eyes and experienced why they acted the way they did, what was it that you were believing to be true that was not?"

Student: "I thought Dad didn't care about me. I thought that he was selfish and only interested in himself. I can now see that he really did love me and had my best interest at heart."

Facilitator: "Give that young boy some love and compassion right now. Can you forgive him for believing a lie?"

Student: "Yes, I forgive him. He did the best he could. I feel sorry that I have wasted so much of my life hating my Dad."

Facilitator: "You have not wasted any time. Because of the belief you have held, you have compensated for feeling unlovable by developing sensitivity and understanding for others who feel unloved. I want you to take a look at the **benefit** for having made that decision."

7. See the benefit - Sometimes seeing the benefit of what has happened diffuses deeply held emotions even further. Seeing the benefit of the situation creates a deeper understanding of how the universe is always working to support our highest good. It is encouraging to know that no matter what happens in our lives, we can be assured that a benefit will occur. Acknowledging that benefit makes us more conscious of what is real and why forgiveness is always expedient. You can actually be happy about

269

an uncomfortable experience when you see that a benefit has come from it. You can actually be grateful for it!

Love and gratitude releases *healing energy* during a Process. Just as when you are doing something you love to do, you have an endless amount of energy. In the same way, your body supports you most when you are happy and filled with appreciation. Healing takes place when the environment supports it. Appreciation is the most healing energy the body can experience. So, the design of The Kalos Process is to do more than eliminate unwanted emotional blocks. <u>It is to reprogram positive information into the circuits of the body, so appreciation can flourish</u>. It is *knowing* and *feeling* the truth in order to be set free.

Make Sure Completion Has Been Achieved

You can always tell when you are complete in a Process because of the peace experienced afterwards. Make sure that there are no held resentments or any kind of negative feelings towards yourself or anyone else when The Process ends. If there are, you will use the "Maturing Up Process" in the next Chapter.

If all is well and you are feeling a sense of relief, you will want to go over what you have learned from the information that came up during The Process. Always review the following list.

    a. What was the perpetration?
    b. What is the truth?

    c. What is the benefit?
    d. What am I to do now?

Consciously reviewing what was gained by The Process will integrate the benefit into your daily life. I am amazed at how "knowing the truth" can change family relationships and up-level your joy in living.

Everyone acts out of what they *feel* is **right, proper or justified,** as described in "The Picture of Man" from *"A New Day In Healing."* My experience of that statement has been born out through taking hundreds of people through The Kalos Process and listening to what THEY are telling me! Very few times is the actual experience exactly as the belief about it. The truth is discovered only after going into the other person's head. Almost always people will do what they believe to be correct or justified. Too many times behavior has been justified when it was inappropriate.

When the negative belief was accurate, there was some kind of drug or alcohol involved. The person was not in their "right mind." Going back and speaking out feelings at the time of the experience creates the space for the truth to show up. Only as we remove the blocks can we change the programming.

Sometimes fear can create the dynamics of an experience to be much worse than it is. Speaking out the feelings and expressing words stuck in your throat, releases the blocks that can hold you bound. Emotions can congest your body and interfere with normal function! You can re-experience from that same perspective and with the same feelings as in the past, only with a new ability to SPEAK

OUT old hurts, owning your part in the episode and seeing the benefit.

When there are residual negative feelings at the end of a Process, you are advised to go to the next Chapter and use the "Maturing Up Process" for completion.

Highlights

• Though many problems are resolved using the Open Eyed Process, the Closed Eyed Process is needed for the following reasons:

a. The original situation or problem goes before conscious memory.

b. Insight is needed with an involved person that requires looking through their eyes to gain an understanding of their behavior.

c. Unresolved emotions need to be cleared.

d. "Generational healing" is wanted to heal family patterns.

• Memorizing the following Steps will make it easier for you to move through the Closed Eyed part of The Process.

1. Student sits, closes eyes and relaxes.
2. Go to the time when the problem began.
3. Identify *feelings* about what happened and Speak out trapped emotions.
4. Walk in another person's shoes and see their viewpoint.
5. Release compassion, understanding and forgiveness.
6. Find the perpetration.
7. See the benefit.

- Always review the following list at the end of every Process.

    a. What was the perpetration?
    b. What is the truth?
    c. What is the benefit?
    d. What am I to do now?

- When there are residual negative feelings at the end of a Process, you are advised to go to the next Chapter and use the "Maturing Up Process" for completion.

Chapter Fourteen

The Maturing Up Process
to Resolve Residual Feelings

Sometimes there are residual feelings left in the body that require more attention and clearing. Even though you go back in time to understand the cause of the problem and reprogram the subconscious mind, some residual feelings may need further understanding for you to prevent old patterns from returning. By understanding the positive intent behind the residual feelings you will be able to mature them up. This is why I call this the "Maturing Up" part of the process. You can use this part of The Process with the Open Eyed, Closed Eyed, or independently at any time. Once learned, it is easily used on yourself.

Another purpose for learning the "Maturing Up" part of The Process is to create internal Advisors to assist you in achieving your goals. Maturing up insecurities and old fears into "daring to risk" to achieve your goals furthers your taking charge of your life in a miraculous way.

The following method of identifying feelings and speaking directly to them can support you in understanding the purpose of their being there. This understanding makes it possible for you to diffuse them at a later time when some of the same programming comes up to haunt you. This gives you more power in being in control. You will be clearer on what those feelings represent and know immediately what to do to take charge of them. The following Steps will help you understand and diffuse residual feelings and emotions, giving you support to keep free of reactionary perpetrations in the future:

1. **Identify and cluster your feelings**.
2. **Give your feelings a form**.
3. **Take the form (Immature Ego State) out in front of you**.
4. **Ask the Immature Ego State questions. ("What do you want?" or "What is your positive intent.")**
5. **Allow the Immature Ego State to answer**.
6. **Love the Immature Ego State**.
7. **Understand the positive intent**.
8. **Understand your feelings**.
9. **Bring in a Full Potential Form to help the Immature Ego State succeed**.
10. **The Full Potential Advisor absorbs the Immature Ego State**.
11. **Create a beautiful Special Place**.
12. **Ask a question or give an assignment to your Full Potential Advisor**.

1. Identify and Cluster Your Feelings — Support your partner to get in touch with all of the buried feelings they have not wanted to feel. Sometimes there is difficulty in doing this because some feelings, like "emptiness," feels like nothing is there. Do not be deceived into believing that you "can't feel your feelings." Everyone has feelings, even though they may be difficult to verbalize at times.

As a child, we all learned to suppress how we felt when deeply hurt. Many times we denied the existence of those feelings, so we would not have to feel the discomfort or pain. The fear of being wrong or being punished for voicing our feelings caused us to stuff or suppress them. A child does not understand that <u>feelings aren't right or wrong, good or bad; they just are</u>!

Often it is one major hidden feeling that discloses a life pattern, such as feeling inadequate, or feeling unloved. Your feelings help you understand **why** you made that decision and lead you to identifying the underlying perpetration.

As feelings are brought together in cluster, a pattern shows up that reveals a person's habitual behavior. You then can see the consistent patterns that affect every area of one's life. Clustering those feelings together into a form makes a powerful image to bring to maturity. We call this form an "Immature Ego State."

2. Give Your Feelings a Form and Color — This is a way of giving something that is abstract or untouchable a form to relate to and communicate with. You can then ask it questions to understand its positive intent. This is seemingly a bit weird, but it works! Parts of this technique were introduced by the father of modern psychology, Sigmund Freud. Since then, it has evolved through transpersonal psychology practitioners, like

Roberto Assagioli and Vernon Woolf. If you do not "see" a form, just sense a form there.

Giving the feelings a form enables you to take charge and do something about your condition. Giving emotions a physical form tells you the intensity and relationship one has with them. For example, the brighter the red an object is, the more anger laden within. When feelings take a pointed or sharp shape they are more intense. Feelings that take the form of a hatchet could mean that the person has deep defensive pain that needs protection. When feelings are black, huge or monsterish, the problem is usually severe or clouded with fear. If the shape is small and light colored, the feelings are usually less intense. We call this form an Immature Ego State.

3. Take the Form (Immature Ego State) out in Front of You — Taking the shape made from the feelings out in front of you creates cooperation so the mind can release and let them go. Usually, a sigh of relief is felt by the person letting go. Having the Immature Ego State out in front of you allows an easier conversation to take place. It helps you detach from your programming.

4. Ask the Immature Ego State Questions — After you have given the feelings a shape, form and color and have taken the form out in front of you, ask the form a question: **"What is your positive intent?"** or "What do you want?" Remember, there is a positive intent behind every feeling. Let it answer you.

By questioning the Immature Ego State, you can find out about its positive intention. You ask it directly <u>what it wants and if it's getting what it wants</u> through its past expression. Actually, you can ask any part of your body if there is a message for you at any time. Even without being in a Process, it will tell you the truth. Try it and be surprised!

After it answers the previous question, ask the form: **"Is it working very well?"**

In other words, will its present form permit the success of its intention. The answer will be obvious. You then ask: **"Are you willing to learn a better way?"**

This gives possibility for future success and awakens you to new choices.

5. **Allow the Immature Ego State to Answer —**
Make sure the Immature Ego State answers your question. Be patient, yet insist on an answer. Usually, the immature form is very anxious for healing. The form will answer you and tell you its positive intent. You can give it a mouth, if need be. Many times the shape is only a colored ball or dark odd shaped blob. It doesn't matter. Go with what comes up, making sure the answer is a positive one. As an example, a form may say, "I don't want to get hurt," thus to be safe. "Being safe" means there is danger around, which is a negative statement. So, go to the intention of being safe and you will find another positive intent. It will probably say, "So I can be happy!" This is more positive. Some common positive intents are:

a. To be loved.
b. To be free.
c. To be happy.
d. To be creative.

6. Love the Immature Ego State — Mentally talk to it and let it know your goodwill is harmless. Be friendly and understanding, never blaming or condescending.

7. Understand the Positive Intent — This is the key to understanding the very purpose behind the feeling and behavior. It is the keynote of The Process. When you understand that <u>behind</u> every action or feeling is a POSITIVE INTENTION, you can transform your ability to express your intentions maturely.

A positive intent represents what you wanted to happen, your hope, your heart's desire. Problems arise when you act out your positive intent with immature (fear based) programming. For instance, a woman wanted to lose weight and tried every kind of diet, but couldn't. Her weight problem began after being sexually assaulted. Staying overweight was to keep her from ever being assaulted again. Her positive intent was to be SAFE and PEACEFUL. Losing weight could make her the object of another assault. Maturity takes place when a positive intention is realized in a full potential way.

8. Understand Your Feelings — By understanding your feelings and their positive intentions, you can be in better charge of your life. Then, when these feelings come up again in the future, you can immediately go to the positive intent. You can continue breaking the old pattern of being a victim of those feelings and taking charge of your life through understanding the true meaning of those feelings and the message they are conveying.

Understanding your own feelings helps you to identify other people's true positive intentions, also. This will support you in your communication and to respond to people's intent rather than solely to their behavior. We gain a deeper understanding for them, as well. *Looking past the act, to its intent, connects people to each other and makes it possible for true communication to take place.* Problems of communication resolve only at a *feeling level*, when those feelings are understood and expressed.

Feelings get us in touch with possible dangers, as well as with love that connects us with each other. They serve a positive purpose by making a loud or soft announcement about something which needs our attention. Having feelings is the mind's way of protecting us with a "wake-up call," to tell us that something is threatening our peace, safety or comfort. As a young child (or adult), our feelings become a wonderful defense system we have for our personal protection.

Giving your feelings a form to talk to them can help you understand them. Sometimes you just need to *listen* to them. The unwanted form can then shift into a mature state automatically or with the assistance of a Full Potential Advisor.

9. Bring in A Full Potential Form to Help the Immature Ego State Succeed — Now you are ready to bring in a Full Potential form to support the immature form to succeed. Every positive intent has a full potential way of expressing itself. As soon as the positive intent is clear, *you bring in an image that could represent that intent in a more beautiful and positive way.*

This newly created form functions as a Full Potential Advisor. This person or symbol can give extraordinary advice from the inner planes of the heart. Make sure the image is someone or something highly regarded and kept in a full potential attitude. A Full Potential Advisor is not something outside yourself that you are inviting in, but simply an aspect of yourself expressed through form.

Many times an image of a heavenly being comes into view. If no image comes into focus, create a magnificent image of a person you have never met or someone uniquely wonderful who can represent your positive intention fully. Often a full potential image of yourself comes in. Just allow whatever occurs to happen in its own natural way. Whatever is appropriate will appear and be perfect for the situation.

10. The Full Potential Form Absorbs the Immature Ego State — Have the Full Potential Advisor stand next to the Immature Ego State. This allows the mind to see where it misjudged the action. You get to see how the intention was the same, but how it expressed itself was very different! The Immature Ego State expressed itself out of fear; whereas, the Full Potential Image is chosen by an adult to represent the true intention maturely. To think that both of these images represented the very same intention is almost unbelievable. To love the immature image for its positive intent is very valuable. It wanted to be the expression of the other image all along, but it just didn't know how to do it. It was too small or too fearful to see the truth.

Absorbing the Immature Ego State into the Full Potential Advisor Matures it to its Full Potential. Have the Full Potential Advisor reach out and absorb the Immature Ego State, making sure that imaging or sensing on the part of the student has supported this. If the Immature Ego State is much larger than the Full Potential Advisor, make them close to the same size, so absorption can easily take place. Now, it can appreciate what it has learned from the past and graduate into its Full Potential of love, peace and joy — what it wanted all along and didn't know how to get. The only love it knew was attached to fear and insecurity.

Once this transformation through absorption has taken place, you then are ready to invite your Full Potential Advisor to your "Special Place." A place deep within you, where you know it's safe because only you and God are there.

11. Create a Beautiful Special Place — The next step is to create a beautiful safe place where you can be reminded and taught by your Full Potential Advisor at any time. In this place you will love relaxing and basking in its beauty and peace. This Special Place can support your continued healing and success. You will love going back there to speak to your Full Potential Advisor and receive guidance in your daily life. You will be reminded of your positive intent behind your feelings. Your Full Potential Advisor can remind you of the very information you need to overcome your unwanted personal and family patterns.

Create the most beautiful, peaceful place that you can imagine. You can have anything there you want. Smell the fresh air. There can be trees, flowers, birds, or whatever you wish. It is your special place. Listen to the water flowing and the sounds of Nature there. This beautiful place that you create, I call "The Kingdom Within." It is here in this state of peace that you can take charge of your life in a powerful way. You can pray, meditate, or contemplate and understand your personal issues with greater clarity. Creating the habit of asking questions and listening for answers gives you new tools to work with in your daily life. Your "Special Place" is just that —

A place of peace and rest where only you can go.
A place where you can receive guidance.
A place where you can contemplate your Purpose
        and how to express it in your Full Potential.

12. Ask a Question or Give an Assignment to Your Full Potential Advisor — This has a positive effect in your daily living. You have Full Potential Advisors, appointed by you, to answer questions and take on assignments concerning all areas of your life. Your own personal Advisors for health, finance, career, and spiritual concerns can be brought into your "Special Place" for guidance and counseling. They will keep you honest and focused on your intentions and help you to get clear about your purpose for living.

You can ask your Advisors any question and they will answer you just as they do during a Kalos Process. Remember, they are only an aspect of yourself and can only assist you in connecting with the Spirit within. You are always in charge. You can even fire them if they do not perform well. You can send them away and have them come back in their full potential again.

Within each of us is a *master* wanting to support our joy in living and our success in life. "Be still and know" is an axiom for our day, as in days of old. Within you is *"the Word"* to answer your daily questions and give support for your daily quests.

Summary and Suggestions to Improve Your Processing

Always make sure that you (and your partner) are at peace when closing The Process and that there are no more issues to be resolved. Unless you experience a level of release, The Process is not complete. All resentments should have left by now. If they haven't, you are not finished with that Process. Sometimes a person wants to stop and pray while in their Special Place. This is fine and I encourage it. When led by the Spirit, I pray with them.

Because this is an intuitive process, you are free to follow inner guidance. Just know that you are complete with the four items mentioned in the previous Chapter before ending the session. Those four items are:

1. What was the perpetration?
2. What is the truth?
3. What is the benefit?
4. What am I to do now?

Helpful Hints

a. Always follow along with whatever information comes up; don't doubt or argue with it. More clarity will be seen as The Process moves along.

b. Really "be there" in The Process and support your partner by repeating what they say, not questioning it. Do all that you can to assist them to become more clear.

c. Use empathy, not sympathy. Do not get "caught up" in their story or perpetration. Your compassion, not collusion, is the model they need to support them to get the best results.

d. Stay clear by studying and understanding the Universal Principles, as taught in *Chapter Fourteen*.

e. The Process does not destroy any feelings or experiences of the past, but helps to understand them. Understanding is the key to loving in a mature way. This is why we "mature up" feelings rather than annihilate them.

f. Encourage and support. Remind them that to the degree they have experienced rejection and pain, is to the same degree they will expand their ability to experience connectedness and peace. To the degree that one has not felt loved, is the same degree one will appreciate love in a greater way.

g. Keep focused on the resolution instead of the problem. Bring them to clarity that their will is in God's Will.

h. Study the Universal Principles. Listen for what doesn't fit. BE HONEST! You transform your lives no faster than you are willing to be honest.

By loving yourself enough you can be open to succeed in any area of your life, particularly when it supports your PURPOSE for LIVING.

No experience is wasted.
There are <u>no</u> failures; that's a perpetration.

The Process Helps You See
Everything as a Benefit

If you saw that everything that has ever happened to you is beneficial, would it change your attitude about your life? Experiment with that possibility. See what happens! Struggling to look for the benefit is rarely needed. When you choose to give thanks in each experience, the benefit usually jumps out at you. Be patient, although your mind doesn't want to be. Your mind's programming is such that it wants everything NOW (or yesterday)!

287

As you practice these steps, you will find it valuable to use on yourself alone, working by yourself, on yourself. You will find a new way to uncover why you feel the way you do and why you act the way you do. You will discover who you are and the wonderful love you are. The Process will support you in being your Full Potential.

All the parts of The Process have a specific meaning; yet they do not have to be in the exact order given in this text. There is flexibility in using The Process. At the end of this Section you will find sheets to aid you in facilitating The Process with others. They are in an abbreviated form. Memorizing the steps will support you to go on your own and experiment on yourself. You cannot hurt yourself and you can have a wonderful, insightful time experimenting!

Highlights

- Residual feelings may need further attention and clearing.

- The following steps are followed to mature up and resolve residual feelings:

  1. Identify and cluster your feelings.

  2. Give your feelings a form. We call this form an Immature Ego State.

  3. Take your feelings (Immature Ego State) out in front of you.

  4. Ask the Immature Ego State questions.

  5. Allow the Immature Ego State to answer.

  6. Love the Immature Ego State.

  7. Understand the Positive Intent.

  8. Understand your feelings.

  9. A Full Potential image comes forward to help the Immature Ego State succeed. This new image represents the very "intention" of the Immature Ego State, except in a more beautiful and positive way.

10. The Full Potential image absorbs the Immature Ego State.

11. Create a beautiful Special Place. I call this the "Kingdom Within." Your Special Place is:

A place of peace and rest where only you can go.
A place where you can receive guidance.
A place where you can contemplate your Purpose and how to express it in your Full Potential.

12. Ask a question or give an assignment to your Full Potential Advisor and let them answer you.

- Within each of us is a "master" wanting to support our joy in living and our success in life.

- Always make sure your partner is at peace when closing The Process.

- Make sure that you are complete with the following four items before ending the session.

  1. What was the perpetration?
  2. What is the truth?
  3. What is the benefit?
  4. What am I to do now?

Chapter Fifteen

Overcoming Interferences
to Completing The Kalos Process

Sometimes an oppressive energy attaches to the electrical field of a person who is already oppressed with problems. The student will feel an oppression, such as a black box above his head, unexplainable emotions, or inability to keep the Immature Ego State from changing forms during a Process. Brugh Joy, author of *"Joy's Way,"* called them "thought forms." Others call them "energy forms" or "entities."

Some suggest that negative energies can attach to a person's aura (energy field) to amplify a subconscious feeling, so that the person can be more aware of what needs healing. Other people point to more sentient energy forms. They refer to them as "unclean spirits," that seek to attach themselves to feed off negative hidden feelings. Still others point to the demonic and how these malevolent forces seek to undermine you. <u>Whatever the form or origin, you can have authority over them and cast them out</u>!

You will want to take charge of that energy in a special way. Having "dominion over the earth . . . and every creeping thing upon the earth" is a teaching from Genesis, the first book of the Bible. I look at the Bible as a blueprint for making life work. All of the laws and principles for living a successful life are contained therein.

Jesus healed many people who were oppressed and possessed with unclean spirits, sometimes called devils. There is a difference between oppressive spirits and possessive spirits. Oppressive spirits attach to the outside of the body in the auric energy field, while possessive ones penetrate inside the body. I am amazed to find so many people oppressed. Sometimes, all they need for healing is to be relieved of this oppression.

I find oppressive energies, or spirits, in conjunction with every serious disease. There are oppressive energies for cancer, diabetes, and AIDS, as well as for all types of emotional ailments, such as anger, confusion, doubt, and fears of all types. Negative energy forms take on the vibration of the problem. You CAN take authority over them yourself, or seek professional support in this area. Your local charismatic church can be counted on to help you, as well as any church that teaches on the "gifts of the Spirit." Study Acts, I and II Corinthians, Romans, and other New Testament Books to gain more understanding and examples of healing in this area.

You can take charge of any emotional energy or oppression, if you can identify it. It is even possible to change a current of energy within your body by command. So, if within the process you find any unusual energy that will not cooperate, have the person take authority over it. Simply say:

"I bind you _____ and take you out and away from my body and send you to the sun (or outer darkness) to be transformed and healed."

You can say whatever is comfortable for you. Some people like to send the oppression to a deep abyss or to God for healing. Just make sure that you identify the energy with a name, like, "spirit of fear, anger, frustration, sickness, etc." You will have the best results when you identify exactly what the oppressive energy is.

You Don't Have to Fear "Unclean Spirits"

I remember when I worked with a beautiful young woman whose pain kept moving around in her body. Unjustifiable pain is another way you can know that a "possessive spirit" is present, besides using MRT. When I realized that this was the problem and confronted her about it, she became upset. Looking into her eyes, I noticed a terrifying energy that made the hair stand up on my arms. Her caring husband, to my surprise, acknowledged he felt this too. He reported to me that an entity had spoken to him in a strange deep voice through her and even warned him not to marry her or it would destroy him. Her health had been bad since their marriage more than three years before. I asked him how he felt about marrying her in this awful circumstance. He replied, "I wanted the challenge!"

Because this was discovered in the middle of a Seminar Weekend, I took her aside to another room. With the aid of a small circle of supportive friends, through the prayer of faith, she repeated the phrase mentioned above, taking authority over the entity inside and surrendering her heart to God. She was freed from this terrible condition. You can imagine how wonderful she felt. She went into the Seminar room with a large smile on her face reporting to the class her wonderful healing - the pain was over!

We used the term: "In the Name of Jesus Christ," for it was Christ who showed us the way to take control over these energies. I still use the name of Jesus Christ to take authority over unclean spirits. Christ taught us to not fear any of these energies. They only accentuate what needs healing within. You may want to have some assistance in the beginning. Oppressive energies will leave quickly, while possessive ones (ones that attach to a physical part inside the body) tend to hang on and require FAITH. You can take authority over them though, in the same way.

You really do have much more dominion than you have ever realized. Now you can test, before and after a clearing, to confirm that the clearing has taken place. Your body has all the information needed to determine what it needs. Through MRT you can determine how many and the exact name of each entity . This speeds up the process and makes it easy for everyone.

Your Word Is Powerful!

When you speak, energy changes! You really are powerful! Of course, you were made in the image of God and have been promised dominion over the earth. You can even change an electrical current in your body through speaking the word. This is demonstrated at Kalos Introductions all the time. You can command unwanted energy to leave as easily as asking a child to please go to his room. You can speak the word to clear your own energy field of negative thought-forms, which are affecting your thoughts and feelings.

Clearing your energy field will help you think more clearly. A "spirit of confusion" can oppress and cloud your mind. I have found dozens of these oppressive energies within individuals. You can ask your body through MRT and find out how many and the names of each one. Simply do a strong test, then state:

"Aura is in the clear."

Use MRT - a strong test means that you do not need clearing. A weak test means that your aura does need clearing. You then test the amount of entities in the aura by saying:

"There are 5 or more, 10 or more, etc.. "

Find the exact number and then you can identify their names by stating them. Remember, the arm will stay strong on a yes, but go weak on a no. After clarifying the number and names, repeat the statement mentioned above or use the suggestion below, or one of your choice to remove them from your body and energy field. In summary:

1. Identify the number and names of negative energies (entities).
2. Call them by name after saying *"I bind you____*.
3. Take them out and away from your body and energy field.
4. Send them to the sun or outer darkness to be changed into loving, complementary energy in the universe.
5. Release healing power of light and love, etc. to take the space of where the negative energy was.

Bind them and cast them out and away, rather than leave them in your environment. You can find more detailed information on this in your local Christian book store. Remember, don't be frightened. You are a powerful being in the universe, much more powerful than some oppressive energy. You can take charge of unwanted oppression and experience freedom by choice.

Potential Names of Negative Energies

Abandonment
Addiction to _____
Anger
Anxiety
Arguing
Arrogance
Bitterness
Bullying
Chatter (inner & outer)
Compulsion
Confusion
Contention

Control
Criticism
Cynicism
Darkness
Death
Dependency on a man
Dependency on a woman
Depression
Discouragement
Disloyalty
Doubt
Envy

Escapism
Fear (Any fear energies)
  Fear of the dark
  Fear of death
  Fear of failure
  Fear of intimacy
  Fear of pain or injury
  Fear of rejection
Frustration
Gossip
Greed
Grief and loss
Hatred of men
Hatred of women
Helplessness
Idleness
Inadequacy
Indecision
Indulgence
Intolerance
Jealousy
Judgmentalness
Lack of confidence
Lack of faith
Laziness
Lying
Loneliness
Lust
Manipulation
Martyrdom
Mistrust
Negativity
Nervousness
Not good enough
Obsession
Oppression
Overwhelm

Pain
Pessimism
Pettiness
Possessiveness
Poverty
Pride
Procrastination
Rebellion
Rejection
Religious
Remorse
Resentment
Sadness
Sarcasm
Schizophrenia
Self-hatred
Self-pity
Sensuality
Sexual compulsion
Shame
Sloppiness
Sorrow
Strife
Stubbornness
Stressful
Survival
Temper
Travail (anguish)
Unbelief
Unfaithfulness
Unforgiveness
Unworthiness
Violence
Weakness
Workaholic
Worry

Highlights

- Oppressive energies can attach to the aura (electrical field) of a person who is already oppressed with problems.

- Negative energy forms take on the vibration of the problem. Every disease and negative emotion has a like counterpart in the form of "thought forms" or entities.

- You CAN take authority over them yourself, or seek professional support in this area.
  One way to do this is to say:
  "I bind you _____ and take you out and away from my body and send you to the sun for healing."

- You don't have to fear unclean spirits. They only accentuate what needs healing within. You may want some assistance in their clearing, though.

- Through MRT you can determine how many and the exact name of each entity, then take them out and away from your body and send them to God, the sun, or outer darkness to be changed into loving, complementary energy in the universe.

- Your word is powerful! You were made in the image of God and have been promised dominion over the earth!

Chapter Sixteen

Sample Processes

The following examples are to support you to see that each Process is as unique as the person being facilitated. While each Process follows the same general outline and adheres to the same principles, the method of getting results will be as varied as the facilitators using them.

The sample Processes in this Chapter are to support you to get a feel for the fluid movement of this highly successful causal healing methodology. If you wish you can practice along with this Process by sliding a piece of paper down covering up the next question by the facilitator. This will allow you to get a "feel" for what you would do next. Then see what the facilitator asked and how it proceeded. You can use The Kalos Process Outline at the end of this Chapter to assist you.

This Process was designed to teach causal healing to the public and professional community. Though it is astoundingly simple, it is profoundly effective. *The names and places of students in the sample Processes have been changed to support confidentiality.*

A Sample Open Eyed Process
That Becomes a Closed Eyed Process

Problem: Fear of Rejection

Goal: To create a successful intimate loving relationship

In the following example Process, a *fear of rejection* was getting in the way of a successful intimate relationship. This beautiful couple went through much emotional pain not understanding that fearing rejection sabotages one's ability to give and receive love. To get too close to someone you love would be risking suffering again. Yet, to not be close is another kind of emotional pain that usually ends up in sickness or separation. The wife discovered her part in sabotaging the relationship through backing off and keeping a distance, all the while believing it was her husband who had a wall up, and believing that he was the one who needed to express more love. Her mind's fear kept her from being intimate and protected her from possible emotional pain. Blame is a good pretender to place the focus somewhere else. The following Process is a good example of how each of us is truly responsible for our experience of someone else. No one can make you suffer emotionally, only yourself.

The following MRT was used to disclose whether the wife was double or single minded in accomplishing her goal.

Wife: "I think I want a successful intimate relationship." [MRT — Strong]
"I feel I want a successful intimate relationship." [MRT — Weak]
"I think I can have a successful intimate relationship." [MRT — Strong]
"I feel I can have a successful intimate relationship." [MRT — Weak]

Both "feeling" tests were weak. She didn't *feel* she even wanted to create a successful intimate relationship on a subconscious level. Her conscious thoughts of course did.

Facilitator: "What is getting in the way of your *feeling* you want to create an intimate love relationship?"

Wife: "I don't know; I guess I am afraid of being rejected."

Facilitator: "That is a possible reason. Let's test it. Do you believe you are afraid of being rejected?"

Wife: "I think I am afraid of being rejected."
[MRT — Strong]
"I feel I am afraid of being rejected."
[MRT — Strong]

Facilitator: "You are single minded that you are afraid of rejection. Let us find out when you made the decision that if you love deeply, you will be rejected. This will tell us what age you are in your capacity to express intimate love.

"Age capacity for expressing intimate love in the Circuit. Circuits in the clear." [MRT — Strong]

"Age of Decision for expressing love is 30 or younger, [MRT — Strong]
20 or younger, [MRT — Strong]
10 or younger, [MRT — Strong]
5 or younger, [MRT — Strong]
4 or younger, [MRT — Strong]
3 or younger, [MRT — Weak]
The age is four."

The emotion points that tested weak at age four were: Frustration, suppressed anger, need for approval, and guilt.
The persons involved with those emotional weaknesses at that age were then tested.

"Think of father, [MRT — Strong]
Think of mother, [MRT — Weak]
Think of brother." [MRT — Weak]

Mother and the new little brother were related to this decision. As soon as the age was identified, the student began remembering the fears and insecurities that surrounded that traumatic time in her life. "Mom was so busy with a new baby that she didn't notice how rejected I felt." Then, on top of feeling unimportant and rejected by mother, Dad leaves Mom with no hope of returning. This created a double whammy that proved to the young vulnerable child that she was not important enough to be loved AND if one loves really deeply the other person may reject you for someone else.

At age four it was the brother, now it is the husband. This also explained why this wife felt so insecure and jealous when her husband would perform his music and be surrounded by other women. She always felt that he didn't want her around. This was **her** tormenting feelings to prove her programming correct, not the reality. When emotional pain or trauma is triggered from an earlier time, one experiences being the very age when that original decision was made. Is it any wonder that grown-ups behave so immaturely at times?

Facilitator: "Close your eyes, image Mother, be age four and speak out your feelings to mother and brother. Tell the truth, letting her know why you feel rejected."

Wife: "You don't care about me anymore! You just want to spend all of your time with Aaron. I feel lonely and rejected by you. Why can't you hold me like you do him?"

Facilitator: "Do you understand why Mother has not been giving you as much attention as usual?"

Wife: "Yes, she was overwhelmed with a new baby and my older brother and me to take care of. Dad was always gone. She had too much to do."

Facilitator: "It sounds like you really understand what it is like to be a busy mother. Can you forgive her for not giving you all of the attention you wanted?

Wife: "Yes, I understand."

Facilitator: "Can you understand how your older brother must have felt when you were born?"

Wife: "Yes, he had to share Mom with me. No wonder he used to get mad at me so much."

Facilitator: "Do you see that your mother really did love you, even though you believed she didn't? How could she do otherwise? You are a mother; is there any way that you could <u>not</u> love your child?"

Wife: "No, I do know she loved me and has always loved me. She has been the one to stand by me in many situations."

Facilitator: "How can you show Mom you love her, even while she is taking care of your baby brother?"

Wife: "I can go to her and hold on to her leg and be with her while she is feeding Aaron."

Facilitator: "Do that right now. How does that feel?"

Wife: "It feels good. I feel close to Mom."

Facilitator: "Wonderful! You see, you could have done that, but you made a decision that you were rejected, so you could never risk the chance of being hurt.

Have some compassion for that little child. She really was *feeling* rejected, even though she wasn't. She went through a lot of emotional pain and did the best she could under the circumstances. (Pause)

Now give some advice to that little girl to help her remember that she **is loved** and doesn't ever need to feel rejected again by those she loves. (Pause)
What was the advice?"

Wife: "For me to be the one to reach out and share my love and stay connected, because I really am loved."

Facilitator: "Yes, that is great. You can be the one to reach out and share. You can remember that the little four year old programming in you was just a fantasy, not reality. You really are loved. That's the truth! What was the

305

BENEFIT of having this dysfunctional programming? You have somehow learned or benefited from this early childhood experience. How?"

Wife: "Well, I have been quiet and listened to people and people feel safe around me. I have always been very careful for others to not feel rejected. And I guess I have learned many ways to be a loving person, so I won't be rejected."

Facilitator: "Very good, you have benefitted much from this four year old decision. You never need to regret any of those experiences, just appreciate the fact that you understand them. You can now open your eyes and we will review your Process."

At this point she opened her eyes and thanked me. She broke through 40 years of debilitating programming that had cost her one marriage and was about to cost her another. She saw how her four year old programming was keeping her from reaching out and sharing more love to the man she loved the most. She identified the reason why she was so uncomfortable in being the one to "reach out" and take responsibility for her relationship. It was her four year old that decided she was not loved, and decided to not take a chance on being rejected. She was now ready to be the one to reach out and take her husband's arm, no matter how many women were surrounding him in a concert. She was now willing to take her rightful place by her King! Feeling like a Queen empowered her to take the throne in her home and in her relationship. A warm glow surrounded her lovely face.

Facilitator: "Now, let us test your programming and see if you have matured that programming up to present time."

"Age Capacity for expressing intimate love is present time."

"Now let us test to see if you are aligned with your feelings and thoughts about wanting to express love maturely."

Wife: "I think I want a successful intimate relationship." [MRT — Strong]
"I feel I want a successful intimate relationship." [MRT — Strong]

"I think I can have a successful intimate relationship." [MRT — Strong]
"I feel I can have a successful intimate relationship." [MRT — Strong]

Sample Closed Eyed Process

The Woman Who Didn't Like Her Mother
Revealing the Truth Freed Mother and Daughter

The following Process was done on the spur of the moment. It was done to give a leader in a wholistic healing organization a demonstration of the Kalos work. Much to her surprise, she was able to understand and heal a longstanding problem with her mother. The following Process is unique, in that she was able to speak to her mother and verify the happenings from Mom's early childhood.

Facilitator: "What would you like to have happen that is not happening?"

Student: "I really don't know, I feel I have done so much healing work in the past. I have been involved in natural healing for over ten years. What do you suggest for you to demonstrate your work?"

Facilitator: "How is your relationship with your parents?"

Student: "I believe my relationship is fine!"

Facilitator: "Since I want to demonstrate how The Kalos process works, and you want me to do a sample Process for you, it really doesn't matter what we use. So let's begin by testing your relationship with your mother and father. Almost all emotional stress that is stored in the body goes back to when you were very young."

Student: "That is fine."

Facilitator: "We first must test and correct the three major electrical circuits in your body, so we can get accurate information from a cellular level. (This was done and found to have no circuits out of balance.)

"Think of father" [MRT — Strong]
"Think of mother" [MRT — Weak]

"Since your mother has tested weak, we will use her for our Process."

Student: "I can't believe that I still have 'stuff' with my mother. I have been working on my relationship with her for ten years!"

Facilitator: "You have probably done much, and apparently there is more to heal. How do you like being with your mother?"

Student: "I can't stand being around my mother!"

Facilitator: "Doesn't that tell you that there is something more to heal?"

Student: "I guess you're right. OK, we'll use my mother for the demonstration."

Facilitator: "How long have you had a problem being around your mother?"

Student: "Since I was very young."

Facilitator: "What is it that bothered you so much?"

Student: "It was the way she treated Dad."

Facilitator: "Close your eyes, relax and think of Mom. How do you feel?"

Student: "I feel irritated and a little angry."

Facilitator: "Tell Mom how you feel. Express all of your feelings, as well as any withholds that might be there."

Student: "I feel really irritated at you, Mom. I don't like the way you treat Dad. You are always raising your voice at him and seem so angry all the time. I hate that!"

Facilitator: "Go to the first time you felt that way. What was going on?"

Student: "I am a young girl and she is hollering at Dad."

Facilitator: "Do you understand WHY she is hollering at Dad?"

Student: "No, she is always acting that way."

Facilitator: "Would you like to understand why?"

Student: "Yes."

Facilitator: "Good. Go around to the back of your mother and look at the back of her head. Now, move right up next to her head; and now, move right inside her head. You won't take anything out that can hurt you in any way. Just be there inside of Mom and look through her eyes at her husband. How is she feeling?"

Student: "She is angry at Dad. It seems to be something about their sexual relationship."

Facilitator: "Go into the bedroom with your husband, sit on the bed, and tell him how you feel."

Student: "I feel so angry at you. You are always wanting sex. You don't care about my feelings."

The student went on to express anger and resentment (on behalf of her mother) for Dad being too sexually minded.

Facilitator: "I sense that this is not the first time that you have had anger and sexuality connected. Go to the first time you felt this way."

Student: "When I was very young." (She opened her eyes and told me that she didn't know anything about her mother's childhood.)

Facilitator: "That is fine, the less you know, the better. It is not the *thinking* mind that has the answers. Just close your eyes and make it up!"

Student: "I believe I am about 5 years old."

Facilitator: "Who is there; and what is going on?"

(A long pause)

Student: "I don't believe this."

Facilitator: "What is happening?"

Student: "My three brothers are molesting me! It's really horrible. I hate this! I can't believe this!"

Facilitator: "You are doing fine, just stay there and tell them how you feel. Tell the truth!"

Student: "I hate you for doing this. I feel ashamed. I feel horrible. I feel confused." (She went on to express all of her feelings out.)

Facilitator: "Move to age seven. Is this type of behavior still going on?"

Student: "Yes."

Facilitator: "Move to age ten. Is it continuing?"

Student: "Yes, with one of my brothers."

The student went on to express that full intercourse went on with one of the brothers during the teenage years. She told the name of the brother and some other incidences to capture as much information as possible. She expressed much anger, fear and shame.

Facilitator: "You have done well. Now, come back to the bedroom where you are talking to your husband. Do you understand WHY you get so angry over sexuality?"

Student: "Yes."

Facilitator: "Now, move outside of Mom and come back into yourself as a child. Do you understand

WHY Mom had such a bad attitude around Dad?"

Student: "Yes, and I feel so sorry for Mom. What a terrible childhood! Could this be true?"

Facilitator: "It is possible, and it really doesn't matter, because what really matters is that you have compassion and understanding for the way Mom treated Dad. Give Mom a hug and ask her to forgive you for being so mad at her for so long."

The lady opened her eyes at that point and asked again, "Could this be true?" I suggested that she ask her mother about it when she saw her. She said that she would. The amazing thing that happened at the end of this Process was that she totally changed her feelings toward her mother from irritation and anger to compassion and love. She actually was anxious to speak to her mother and find out what REALLY happened.

I received a call that night from this student. She excitedly told me that as soon as she walked in the door from seeing me, the phone rang. Guess who it was? Yes, it was Mother! The conversation that followed verified every detail of The Process with the mother in awe saying, "How did you know? I have never told a soul, not even your father!"

Needless to say, "Know the truth, and the truth shall set you free," is as valuable today as in days of old. This lady healed a lifelong problem with her mother through "seeing" with her mind's eye. She now loves to be with her mother, because the maturity of understanding destroyed the "hiding" and made it possible to BE REAL with each other.[20]

Secrets build walls, sharing the truth breaks them down. When the "truth" is known, blaming ends. Blame is a smoke screen that hides reality by focusing in the wrong direction.

---

[20] A short description of this story is used in Book One, *A New Day In Healing*, *Chapter Ten*, page 127 to understand how perpetrations form.

Sample Closed Eyed Process

Healing the Consequences of Molestation

The following dialogue began after the testing and correcting of the Three Major Electrical Circuits in the body, as shown in *Chapter Six*. Both the one being tested and the Facilitator must be in electrical balance in order for the testing to be accurate. The tail bone circuit was out of balance in the following example, which revealed the possibility that the sexual organs were out of electrical balance also.

In the following example, a complete Kalos wholistic physical examination was given first, even though the student felt her problem stemmed from an emotional cause. She also complained of neck, lower back and head pain. Sometimes the body will want another part aligned before the emotional work can be completely successful. Electrical interferences can prevent the new information from encompassing the whole body to place it in a healing mode.

A Kalos wholistic physical examination gives a blueprint of the body's inner functioning and discloses imbalances that could be contributing to the problem. Some other common imbalances include vitamin and mineral deficiencies, organ imbalance, hormone imbalance, blood sugar imbalance, lymphatic congestion, and structural imbalances, such as the atlas, the axis and the Temporal Mandibular Joint (TMJ).

Further testing revealed the exact order that the body wanted to be corrected for fastest results. This is called "Priority Testing."

The first priority that came up in the following case was "Emotional." Therefore, the following is a step by step account of that process. Even though the main intent of our meeting had already been discussed, I still used MRT to determine specific intentions and to see if she was aligned in both right and left brain hemispheres (*thoughts* and *feelings*).

Facilitator: "What is it you want to have happen that is not happening?"

Student: "I want to allow myself to feel my sexual feelings and stop being afraid of them. I believe this is the only way I can have a happy, successful sexual relationship with my husband."

Facilitator: "Let us test to see if you are single or double minded about this. Repeat after me as I test you."

The Facilitator makes a statement that reflects the goal of the student, then has them repeat it using MRT.

"I *think* I **want** to have a happy, successful sexual relationship with my husband." [MRT — Strong]

317

"I *feel* I **want** to have a happy, successful sexual relationship with my husband." [MRT — Weak]

"I *think* I **can** have a happy, successful sexual relationship with my husband." [MRT — Weak]

"I *feel* I **can** have a happy, successful sexual relationship with my husband." [MRT — Strong]

Facilitator: "What is getting in the way of your *feeling* that you want to have a successful sexual relationship with your husband?"

Student: "The only thing I can think of is that I am afraid of *feeling* sexual. I am afraid of being overwhelmed or controlled by him. I am afraid of being vulnerable."

Facilitator: "It sounds like something has happened in your past to cause this fear. What was it?"

Student: "At the age of 6 or 7, I was molested by my grandfather." (Tears began to form.) "I have done therapy on this, but it hasn't seemed to help."

Facilitator: "This is probably because you have never matured your ability to express your feelings since you were that age. Any time a decision is made with great emotion, and you must have had a lot of emotion at that time, it becomes the rule of action from that time forth until it is understood and matured up."

The student went on to tell more details of her story and how she told her mother about the incidence right afterward. Her mother did not help; she just told her not to tell anyone and acted angry at her. This only added to her guilt and shame. She was left to feel unprotected from both a man (grandfather) and a woman (mother). This went on to interfere with her trusting either sex, as well as question her own ability to be heard.

Facilitator: "Repeat after me, 'I *think* I am afraid to say how I feel." [MRT — Strong]

"I *feel* afraid to say how I feel." [MRT — Strong]

Her mind was aligned in both *thoughts* and *feelings* that she could not express her feelings, let alone FEEL them!

Facilitator: "Let us test you to locate the exact age when you decided that you could not express your feelings. This will give us the 'age capacity' of you being able to express your feelings."

"Age capacity to express your feelings, in the circuit. Circuits in the clear.
Age 30 and younger, [MRT — Strong]

319

> 20 and younger, [MRT — Strong]
> 10 and younger, [MRT — Strong]
> 5 and younger, (The first weak test here)
> Age 8 and younger, [MRT — Strong]
> 7 and younger, [MRT — Strong]
> 6 and younger" [MRT — Weak].

Age 7 was the age of decision, for it was the youngest strong test. Remember, a strong test is "yes" and a weak test is "no."

We went on to find that the exact age was seven and three quarters. By locating the exact age the memory banks of the mind were able to recall more information to support the process of resolution. This age confirmed that the molestation was the exact age when the present time problem began. She remembered that it happened during warm weather. MRT was used to confirm this.

Facilitator: "Age 7 in the circuit, circuits in the clear."

The eight Emotion Points were tested to identify what emotions were involved. See *Chapter Eight* for a diagram and description. Seven of the Points were out of balance. The testing of these Emotion Points brought up more emotions, which were relevant to the problem. We then proceeded to test the people involved.

> "Think of grandfather [MRT — Weak]
> Think of mother [MRT — Weak]
> Think of father [MRT — Strong]
> (Father was away when this incidence happened.)

Think of grandmother" [MRT — Weak]

This pre-testing gave us the vital information of who was involved, so their relationships could be healed during The Process. Ultimately, it is the healing of relationships that create your personal healing and allows transformation to take place.

The woman relaxed and we began the Closed Eyed part of The Process. The Kalos Process uses <u>no</u> induction, as hypnosis, but simply goes to the time when the problem began; The Process identifies what is going on and Speaks out the feelings to the persons involved; walks in the other persons shoes to understand their positive intent; finds the pattern and the perpetration; "discovers the truth" to be set free; sees the benefit.

Facilitator: "Close your eyes and relax. Go to age 7, right after the molestation took place. How are you feeling?"

(Short period of silence)

Student: "Horrible, ashamed, sad, angry."

Facilitator: "Speak out those feelings to your grandfather. Tell him what you couldn't tell him then, because you were too frightened and confused."

The woman spoke out her hurtful feelings, as if she were still the young child, telling her grandfather how awful that was for him to do that. She raised her voice and expressed her pain well.

She then went on to express her feelings to her mother, who had gotten angry at her and would not let her talk about it to anyone. Feeling unprotected by Mother, she then spoke to her grandmother, telling her that she should have looked out for her also, and protected her from such a person.

Facilitator: "Give love and compassion to the little girl that went through so much pain. She did the best she could at the time. She didn't know how to express her feelings, especially when Mother would not let her. Love her and comfort her."
(Paused for a few moments, allowing her time.)

Facilitator: "Focus on your grandfather again, Do you understand **why** your grandfather did that awful thing to you?"

Student: "Yes, he was drunk."

Facilitator: "Do you understand why he drinks so much?"

Student: "No, he's just a coward!"

Facilitator: "Would you like to understand why?"

Student: "Yes."

Facilitator: "Just walk around to the back of him and look at the back of his head. Move up to just behind his head. Now, move right inside his head, knowing that *you won't take anything out that can hurt you in any way.* Look through his eyes and see the image of little Molly at seven years old. Just be him, now, and get in touch with your feelings. How are you feeling as you look at your little granddaughter?"

Student (as Grandfather): "I feel terrible, ashamed! I feel sorry for what I have done."

Student (as self): "<u>Oh my! He didn't know it was me! Now, I know why I always feel that my partner does not know me</u>!"

Facilitator: "Speak out all of your feelings to your little grandchild. Tell her how you really feel."

Much emotion came up. He was filled with sorrow and shame, as he asked her for forgiveness. Then I suggested that she do some vicarious inner healing for her deceased grandfather in the following manner.

Facilitator: "Staying in grandfather, was this the very first time you have felt shame, or was there an earlier time?"

Student: "There was an earlier time."

Facilitator: "How old are you when that happened?"

Student: "I am 6 years old and my father just beat me. I am angry and ashamed. He said that I don't do things right."

Facilitator: "Speak out the feelings that you couldn't speak out then, because you would have gotten into more trouble."

Student: "I am afraid to do that."

Facilitator: "Tell your father that you are afraid, and keep talking. Tell him all your feelings."

Student: "I am afraid to tell you anything, because I don't want you to beat me more. I feel terrible that you expect so much of me. I can't do any better. You have to teach me how. I want you to love me and it feels like you don't love me when you beat me."

Facilitator: "Do you understand **why** your dad acted that way? Why did he beat you?"

Student: "Yes, he believed I deserved it. He believed that was the way to raise children. He didn't understand how I *felt*."

Facilitator: "That was very harsh punishment for such a little boy, wasn't it?"

Student: "Yes."

Facilitator: "That was a strong belief system that Dad had to make his children do better, wasn't it?"

Student: "Yes, and he treated all the kids that way."

Facilitator: "Love the little boy and have compassion for his pain and for not being understood."

(Pause)

Facilitator: "What decision did you make at that time that began a pattern for your life?"

Student: "I'm not understood and I don't like to *feel* my feelings. <u>Feelings hurt</u>."

(Note: This is the same pattern as Molly, who wanted help to be able to feel her sexual feelings.)

Facilitator: "Notice how this pattern stayed with you as you grew older. Come back to when Molly was seven. Is this why you would escape feeling your feelings through alcohol as you got older?"

Student: "Why, yes!" "When I got drunk, I didn't have to feel. My feelings were numbed!"

325

This is where the family pattern that plagued my student became very apparent to her. This was a great breakthrough for her to see how deeply a family pattern was that she came in to heal.

Facilitator: "Can you see that running from your feelings, instead of expressing them has caused some other problems in your life?"

Student: "Yes, it felt really good to speak them out. I feel much better now."

Facilitator: "Staying in grandfather, cluster all of those feelings and give them a shape, a form, a color. Who or what do they look like?"

Student: "A red amoeba type looking form."

Facilitator: "Give it a mouth and ask it what its positive intention is. Behind every feeling is a positive intent."

Student: "To have a better life, and to share my love."

Facilitator: "That's a wonderful positive intention! Is it working very well?"

Student: "No!"

Facilitator: "Ask it if it is willing to learn a better way to have a better life and share your love."

Student: Asks, then answers, "Yes."

Facilitator: "Since the form, 'the Immature Ego State,' is willing to learn a better way, bring in a Full Potential Image of having a better life and sharing your feelings of love. Who or what does that look like?"

Student: "It is an angel. A beautiful white angel."

Facilitator: "Have the angel stand next to the red amoeba looking shape, and notice that they both represent the very same *positive intent*. It's just that the amoeba was placed there by a small boy who didn't know how to share his love and wanted a better life.
             "Love both of the images and have the angel *absorb* the Immature Ego State." (Pause)

             "Ask the angel to go throughout Grandpa's body and heal all of the residual pain from his youth, the fear and anger, the shame and the guilt. Now ask the angel to 'be there' for grandpa no matter where he is in the universe to teach him understanding and how to express his feelings maturely."

The Student, Molly, sends the angel to her grandfather. This is a sort of blessing, returning love for pain. The spiritual aspect of The Process is the key to transforming our actions from the mind's fear to the

spirit's unconditional love. <u>Healing</u> one's enemy is truly
an act of agape (unconditional) love.

Facilitator: "Molly, now go to the time when you were
seven years old again; leave grandfather's
body and come back to being yourself again.
Look at grandfather. Can you understand why
grandpa acted that way?"

Student: "Yes, I understand."

Facilitator: "Can you forgive him?"

Student: "Yes, I can."

Facilitator: "How has having that experience helped you
in your life?"

Student: "I have a deep empathy and understanding for
others who have been molested or emotionally
abused. I am compassionate and a deeply
sensitive person."

Facilitator: "Good! You see how you actually have been
blessed by this awful experience. To the
degree that you have experienced confusion,
suffering and pain, is to the degree that you
will have the depth of capacity to experience
its opposite — understanding, peace and
love."

"Now, go to a time that you felt you could not express your sexual feelings. What is going on?"

Student: "I am being pushed into having sex when I don't want to."

Facilitator: "How do you feel about that?"

Student: "I feel awful. I feel angry, hurt and sad. I feel like I can't make myself feel different, even though I love him. I feel hate and love at the same time."

Facilitator: "Speak out your feelings and tell him the truth."

Student: "I am really tired tonight. I don't want to make love now. I am confused about my feelings because I love you and want you to love me, but I feel forced into doing something I don't want to do; I feel really uneasy about this. And I FEEL THAT YOU DON'T KNOW ME!"

Facilitator: "Yes, that is the exact pattern that has made you feel so uneasy about your sexual feelings, isn't it? To make love with someone who doesn't know who you are is very unsettling to say the least.

"You are doing a good job speaking out your feelings. How does that feel?"

Student: "It feels really good to let them out. I feel so much clearer. To think that I was not in touch with the feeling that my partner doesn't know who I am, is really a breakthrough for me. I have not honored my feelings, because I didn't even know what was there."

Review: After releasing all of the feelings buried deep inside of her and telling the truth to her mate, she made the connection between her seven year old that knew grandpa didn't even know it was her, to realizing that the big trauma in having sexual relations with her own husband carried with it the scars of that little child. This discovery got her in touch with why she felt so uneasy and even afraid to allow herself to have sexual feelings - for who she is with doesn't know who she is!

Facilitator: "Notice how that pattern has shown up in your life. Notice how sharing the feelings that you <u>could</u> get in touch with made it possible to reach the feelings that were hidden. What would have been different if you could have shared your feelings and told the truth?"

Student: "I would not have held on to my pain so long, always becoming afraid to even *feel* my *feelings*, let alone share them."

Facilitator: "Do you see that because you were able to share your feelings, you were able to resolve some of the problem?"

Student: "Yes."

Facilitator: "What family pattern has made it difficult for you to share your *feelings*?"

Student: "Wanting to escape the pain of even *feeling* my *feelings* because of a belief of being inadequate."

Facilitator: "State the truth! Was grandfather really inadequate when he made that decision as a small boy?"

Student: "No, and I sense that he felt that his father did not understand him, or you could say KNOW HIM."

Facilitator: "Good, you understand how this family pattern has affected your life, and what you came to heal. The truth is: YOU REALLY ARE ENOUGH and YOUR HUSBAND DOES KNOW WHO YOU ARE (Probably more than anyone else)! Is that correct?"

Student: "Yes (smiling)."

331

Facilitator: "Create a Full Potential Advisor for yourself to assist you in identifying and sharing your feelings in a full potential way, since you have sent the angel to your grandfather to assist him in getting in touch with his feelings. Now, you will have your own assistant and advisor."

(Pause)

"What does it look like?"

Student: "She is a beautiful spiritual being with passion and understanding."

Facilitator: "Wonderful! Ask her if she will help you bring trust and spirituality into your sexual life."

Student: "Yes, she will."

Facilitator: "Ask her if she will be there for you 24 hours a day, seven days a week to teach you everything you want to learn about honoring and sharing your feelings, as well as relaxing and enjoying a successful sexual relationship with your husband."

Student: "Yes, she wants to help."

Facilitator: "Give her an assignment to go throughout your body and heal all of the hurts and scars of the past. She has the ability to absorb all the past hurts, just like she did the Immature Ego State. Ask her to clear your body right now and then to work at deeper levels for 15 minutes every day for the next few weeks until all the hurt memories of the past are gone or matured up. Will she do this?"

Student: "Yes, she is happy to."

(Pause, for her to begin this assignment.)

Facilitator: "Great! Now, create a beautiful place for her to dwell. The most beautiful place that you can imagine. You can have anything there you want, trees, grass, waterfalls; whatever you desire and you choose."

(Pause for her to create a Special Place.)

Facilitator: "Tell me what it looks like."

Student: "It is beautiful, green mountains, a stream, grass and flowers. It is so peaceful."

Facilitator: "That sounds beautiful. Now, make a round table for her with big comfortable chairs around. Make it the most beautiful table that you can imagine."

(Pause)

333

"Make sure that she stays in her Full Potential. This is your Special Place and you can invite anyone there you wish. Just make sure that they only come to visit in their *full potential*."

Student: "OK."

Facilitator: "You, also can be there in your Full Potential. You can even invite your grandfather's angel there once in a while to check things out. This is your Special Place to do as you wish. I call it, "The Kingdom Within." Now I would like you to ask your Advisor what you can do to heal your sexual problem with your husband. Speak directly to her."

Student: "What can I do to heal my problem and be able to have a successful sexual relationship with my husband?"   (Pause)

Facilitator: "What did she say?"

Student: "To honor my feelings and share them; to resolve any conflict before we go to bed, and to connect with my husband eye to eye."

Facilitator: "That sounds like good advice to me, doesn't it to you?"

Student: "Yes, that amazes me that she can direct me so easily."

Facilitator: "Are you willing to take her advice and follow through?"

Student: "Yes."

Facilitator: "Isn't it wonderful that you have the answers right inside of you. I hope that you will go to your Special Place and talk to your Advisors on a daily basis. To begin with go there daily. Then, you can go once or twice a week."

Student: "OK."

Facilitator: "Can you see that your Sexual Advisor is spiritual in nature, wanting your sexuality to take on a **quality** rather than a quantity to be a full potential expression of loving?"

Student: "Yes, that is very clear. I like that."

Facilitator: "On the count of three, I am going to ask you to open your eyes:

1. Be aware of your body and come back to this room.

335

2. Appreciate WHO you are, that you are a beautiful child of God who wants to live a full potential life and resolve all of your sexual and relationship problems.

3. Open your eyes and stretch."

This Process began a series of soul searching and profound effects. Through understanding, forgiveness and love any problem can be overcome and healed. Molly was a wonderful example of this.

NOTE:

The following outline may be photocopied to assist you in personally practicing The Process. You may copy it for use in your health practice, as long as credit is given to: "Be Healed! — Transformational Healing Series, Book Two by Dr. Valerie Seeman Moreton." If you want to re-print this or publish it in any form please contact KALOS Publishing 1-800-77KALOS for permission. Thank you very much.

THE KALOS PROCESS
AN OUTLINE OF ITS COMPONENTS

WHERE YOU ALWAYS BEGIN: NAME A PROJECT—
Identify what you want to happen that's not happening.

1. DOUBLE MIND TESTING — Do a think - feel test.

    I think I want . . .   I think I can . . .
    I feel I want . . .   I feel I can . . .

    CONTINUE THE THINK — FEEL TESTING with a question. "What is getting in the way?" Keep asking back the information that the student gives until understanding is achieved.

2. TEST AGE OF DECISION OR ONSET — Ask how long this has been a problem to get an idea of where to begin testing an age. Place the project in circuit and state:

    "Age 20 and younger,
    Age 10 and younger, etc.," until you identify the correct age. This will give you the age of capacity to function in relation to what is in the circuit.

3. DYSLEXIA TESTING — Look at the "X" and the "**II**" with that age in the circuit.

4. TEST THE EMOTION POINTS AT THE AGE OF DECISION. State the age in the circuit and state: "Circuits in the clear."

5. TEST **WHO** WAS INVOLVED AND **WHAT** WAS GOING ON — for you to have made the decision you did.

6. IDENTIFY WHAT HAPPENED AND HOW YOU FEEL ABOUT IT. SPEAK OUT YOUR FEELINGS! Hold the Neuro-vascular Holding Points — Use hands over forehead when emotions surface.

7. FIND THE PERPETRATION — SEE THE TRUTH! What were you believing to be true that was not true?

8. SEE THE BENEFIT OF THE EXPERIENCE — This is an important part of The Process to be seen clearly.

When the experience goes before conscious memory — Use the full Closed Eyed Process and begin at the age when the problem began.

9. RETEST TO MAKE SURE EVERYTHING IS IN ALIGNMENT.

10. CREATE A PLAN FOR CONTINUED RESULTS.

The Kalos Closed Eyed Process

1. SIT WITH RELAXED BREATHING; CLOSE EYES. PLACE HANDS OVER FOREHEAD POINTS.

2. GO TO THE AGE/TIME WHEN THE PROBLEM BEGAN.
   a. What is going on?
   b. Who is there?

c. How do you feel about it?

d. Where do you feel those feelings in your body?

3. IDENTIFY FEELINGS AND SPEAK OUT TRAPPED EMOTIONS. Tell the truth about how you feel to the person there.

4. WALKING IN ANOTHER PERSON'S SHOES.

a. Do you understand why they acted that way?

b. Go into that person's head to understand and identify their thoughts and feelings and intention.

5. RELEASE COMPASSION, UNDERSTANDING AND FORGIVENESS.

6. FIND THE PERPETRATION — SEE THE TRUTH.

7. SEE THE BENEFIT OF THAT DECISION. Express compassion and understanding. Appreciate the experience and how it helped you to survive.

IF COMPLETION HAS NOT BEEN ACHIEVED — Use the Maturing Up part of The Kalos Process. You may want to create a beautiful place anyway with an Advisor to give you answers to questions.

The Maturing Up Part of The Kalos Process

When There are Residual Emotions
at the End of the Previous Process

1. IDENTIFY AND CLUSTER YOUR FEELINGS.

2. GIVE THE FEELINGS A SHAPE, FORM, COLOR. Who or what do they look like?

3. TAKE THE SHAPE OUT IN FRONT OF YOU.

4. ASK THE IMMATURE EGO STATE QUESTIONS:
"What is your positive intention?"
"Is it working very well?"
"Are you willing to learn a better way?"

5. LISTEN TO IT ANSWER EACH QUESTION.

6. LOVE THE IMMATURE EGO STATE FOR ITS POSITIVE INTENTION.

7. UNDERSTAND THE POSITIVE INTENT.

8. UNDERSTAND YOUR FEELINGS. Have compassion for the child that created that survival mechanism.

9. CREATE A FULL POTENTIAL FORM to help the Immature Ego State succeed. What does it look like? Notice they both represent the same Positive Intent!

10. ABSORB THE IMMATURE EGO STATE.

11. CREATE A BEAUTIFUL SPECIAL PLACE AND INVITE YOUR FULL POTENTIAL ADVISOR THERE.

12. ASK IT A QUESTION AND/OR GIVE IT AN ASSIGNMENT FOR THE NEXT 24 TO 48 HOURS.

Always end The Process in a peaceful state. Let the student or partner have the experience of allowing the peaceful healing energy to flow through their muscles, bones, tissues, or any other area. Remember, gratitude is the most healing energy (8.0 cycles) of the body.

SECTION IV

BEING AT CAUSE❓

By Choosing to Take Responsibility for
Your Life from a Nonjudgmental State
— The Universal Principles

*Enjoying the process of living life fully as if it were a
wonderful classroom, a laboratory for experimenting,
learning, discovering and creating.*

Chapter Seventeen

Axioms for Wellness

The following axioms I call "*Universal Principles*," which function beyond the logical perceptions and judgments of the limited mind. They consider the powerful essence of WHO we are as eternal spiritual beings. Therefore, these Universal Principles are illogical to a mind whose main purpose is survival. They may even intimidate that part of our mind that needs to be "right" or "comfortable" to survive.

The mind thrives on exactness and judgment, which serves us fine, as long as it doesn't rule our lives. Consequently, the mind does not like to be at the effect of paradoxes[21] where two opposing viewpoints may be true. Secondly, it doesn't like to be at the effect of irony[22] - something being true sometimes, under some views, and not true at other times. The mind's job is to store and sort all the information that has ever happened to us. Therefore, it *thinks* and *feels* that it knows best. It was never intended for the mind to make our choices for us. That is the job of spirit.

---

[21] a statement or proposition seemingly self-contradictory or absurd but in reality expressing a possible truth.
[22] Expressing a meaning which is different from, and often the direct opposite of the literal meaning.

Owning Your Experience of People and Situations

You are the author of your experience. The fastest way I heal an upset is to ask myself: "Why did I create that?" Without understanding these principles I could buy into a student's perpetration and not be able to coach them appropriately. *The greatest wrong as a counselor or friend is to tell a person they are not responsible for their problem or circumstances.* Colluding[23] with them makes it difficult for you to support them to see what is truthful to heal the cause. People create their experience of life, yet when they have a problem they commonly believe that someone or something "did it to them." Blame is a way of escaping responsibility. As long as the problem is seen to be outside yourself, you are unable to affect it; therefore, not responsible. Even when you identify the problem within, your mind by itself cannot change itself. Your attitude creates much of your experience. Renewing your mind requires observation from another level of functioning - *Spirit, being at Cause!*

Once you uncover more of your subconscious programming, you might discover that it has caused many unwanted events, including accidents and diseases. Open to the possibility that you are creating life to happen to you and around you, not it creating you. Are you willing to experiment?

---

[23]Collude - A secret understanding between two people prejudicial to another. (Webster's Encyclopedic Dictionary)

Going beyond Judgment
to Understand the Positive Intent

The Universal Principles are also valuable in looking at life from another person's viewpoint to understand behavior, a necessary part of The Kalos Process. They help you in discerning life situations and in avoiding premature judgments.

These principles provide a multifaceted perspective that I found myself using to assist people in getting to the source of their problem. Much of the time an upset occurred because one person was not understanding where the other person was coming from; they didn't understand each other's "positive intent." To be able to discern easily another's positive intention requires looking at all levels of consciousness and avoiding "drawing a conclusion before all the facts are known."

Looking at life situations and people's underlying intentions through spiritual eyes can awaken you to seeing the harmlessness of reality, up-level your attitude and help you to renew your mind. Maturing and renewing your mind happens when you can look at life's issues through nonjudgmental eyes, rather than judgmental beliefs that were set, mostly by the age of six. Compassion and love are at the heart of every healing.

A New Context for Healing and Preventing Problems

You can easily look at the physical laws of *Cause and Effect* and identify with *The Mental Precepts,* though some may surprise you. Not so easily examined are the possibilities of a nonjudgmental state.

Looking for the cause of a problem means finding a physical law that was broken, a misconception that boggled the mind, or a spiritual principle abused. Consequences (seen and unseen) always are present in the breaking of any law, whether known or unknown. Locating the CAUSE of any problem may compel you to *s t r e t c h* beyond the limits of your mind! Seeing through the nonjudgmental eyes of spirit can renew your mind - hence *The Universal Principles.*

An Invitation to Live the Principles

These Principles emerged from insights I repeated in Seminars. Most came from previous teachers I met along my path, while some just popped up spontaneously. Some will be familiar. They are not meant to be absolutes to add to your belief system, only possibilities. They are some frames of reference to look at life, like looking through a magnifying lens. You are invited to take a look at life through these new *glasses* and see resolutions from a different viewpoint. By applying the following axioms you will be much more prepared to coach others. Causes and consequences are exposed, as well as how to **apply** these principles to your own life.

UNIVERSAL PRINCIPLES are meant to provide a new paradigm about Life. They help create a new context for the content of your life to show up. They are a way of understanding universal processes. They are listed in this text for helping you utilize The Kalos Process as a premise, not to add to your belief system.

UNIVERSAL DECLARATIONS, derived from these Universal Principles are found at the end of each Principle. They are an invitation to express life in a new context. They are meant to inspire us to live transformed lives and BE our full potential. Feel free to add more of your own. God bless you as you study these Principles and Declarations. See how they work for you!

Universal Principles

1. The Only Constant in Life Is Change

Life never stands still. It is constantly changing like the seasons. On the form side of life the only predictable thing is change itself. Living life happily is about handling change well. While the mental and physical parts of life are exuberant, the essence of life is a constant, "a flowing" that you can depend on. The Paradox is: "The only constant in Life is change itself."

When you resist change and try to hold on to something the way it was, you cause blocks and tension in your body. Resistance interferes with the proper flow of life by trying to "push the river" or slow things down. Stress and tension develop. Anxiety builds when you fear your needs will not be met. You get out of timing with life, and are thrown into a "wake-up" call by the body. This can lead, for example, to stiffness in the joints and a blocked or inflamed intestinal tract. Accidents are also a signal to slow down and align with the proper timing of life.

Resistance to change can also affect conditions relating to the liver, the largest and one of the most important internal organs. You will find many chronic problems begin in the liver. Flexibility to change shows up with limber joints and healthy bowel action.

Change pushes us to look for deeper meaning and expanded benefits in life. It keeps us moving, evolving, growing, trusting. Change threatens the mind's need for the comfort of consistency. Though change challenges our

ability to trust, it provides the opportunity to grow spiritually; for trust is an act of faith.

"Faith is not our ability to believe,
but trusting God's ability to deliver."

*"I welcome beneficial change to deepen
my trust and foster choices that help me
grow."*

2. Whatever We Resist Persists

Resistance creates tension, which blocks the energy
from flowing and causes problems to continue! Cup your
fingers together and pull them against each other. The
harder you pull, the more tension, and the more they bind
together.

Tension does not leave by resisting it; only by
relaxing the tensed area will it release. Neither does
anything go away when we ignore it, only our attention
goes away. The body/mind will then increase the tension
until the deeper issue is heard. Tension builds; it does not
lessen through time by getting used to it. The
consequences are enormous: Headaches, stiffness and pain
in joints, colon and circulation problems, respiratory
problems, irritability and inability to handle emotional
stress.

You can grow beyond resistance, learn the lesson,
and move on. Even pain leaves when you stop resisting it.
Pain is a signal from the body that something needs attention. When you understand the message your body wants

351

to give you, *be free to experience it*, the pain (signal) stops. This is for the vast majority of cases. I realize there may be an exception to this, as with every rule or principle in the universe.

Accept what is going on in the moment by choosing it. Then, let go and flow with life. Acceptance does not mean condoning, it means understanding. Acceptance does not mean resignation and inadequacy, it means that you are open for new choices.

> *"I flow in harmony with life by trusting and accepting, instead of resisting."*

3. The Flow of the Universe Is from Being... to Doing... to Having

You have heard the saying, "Go with the flow!" There is truth in this and a deeper wisdom behind it. Wally Minto[24] in his *Results Book* has given us a model of how the universe flows from being — to doing — to having. I find this a great experiment. Try it! Just choose to BE (whatever you want) and see if that doesn't motivate you to <u>do</u> what supports it. Notice how much easier life is in this flow. When we refer to the "flow of the universe" we really are referring to the flow of the Spirit. The mind has a different flow to it. It is the doer, many times wanting to push the river of life or dam it, rather than flow with it.

---

[24]Wally Minto, founder of Alpha Awareness, has authored several books on transformation.

If you notice how the mind keeps wanting <u>more</u>, <u>better</u>, and <u>different</u>, you will discover that it can never be satisfied. You can never <u>do</u> enough or <u>have</u> enough. There is only temporary fulfillment in "having" things to be happy or "doing" things to be happy. There is only CHOOSING to BE happy, then doing what a happy person does.

When your mind rather than Spirit leads your life, you struggle through the anxiety of "never enough." Suffering is the result of blocking the natural flow of love, peace, joy and all the fruits of the Spirit. Worry, doubt, fear and struggle produces more of the same. Going against the flow of life can lead to problems with overwhelm, anxiety, insomnia, panic attacks, poor or blocked circulation and lymph system congestion. Your body reveals the blocks that you emotionally hold on to.

Going with the flow makes life easier. Your programming is running all the time. Therefore, stop often and enter into silence. Honestly re-looking at the situation can let you know where you are coming from at any moment. Remind yourself often to stop and notice what you are doing and notice how you feel when you feel that way. This awareness moves you out of a programmed state of being into consciousness (spirit).

> "<u>I am</u> a success. Therefore I <u>do</u> what successful people do and <u>enjoy</u> the rich inheritance."

353

4. Love Is the Basis of All Reality

Love is at the source of all creation - the magnetism that holds everything together. When you look behind a person's behavior to their positive intent, you will always find love in some form, though not always expressed in a full potential way. Love is at the foundation of all action, no matter how it may appear on the surface.

All is love, whether expressed from the conditional mind or from the spirit. The Greeks had several words for love, establishing a distinction between the conditional loves of the mind and the unconditional love of the Spirit. Spiritual love they called, *"Agape."*

Your mind expresses love in many ways; from indifference to sacrifice. Indifference is a kind of love that comes from being wounded, from fearing being hurt. Not wanting to be hurt is simply a way to love yourself.

Every action comes out of self love automatically, even without thinking about it. You are programmed this way for survival. Even suicide is committed out of love. A person can love himself so much that he does not want to live a painful or uncomfortable life, or perhaps staying alive would jeopardize the life or comfort of someone they love.

Self love is important for self-esteem. Just don't get stuck there and turn it into self-centeredness. Self-centered love has self-defeating consequences when it doesn't expand to loving others as well. Narcissism and guilt can be the result. People who carry guilt feel better when they are punishing themselves in some way. This is when pain can feel good. Some even become masochists and take pleasure in enduring physical abuse. When you love yourself enough, you then will open to someone else loving you too. As love expands, you will want to commit to another's happiness, as well as your own. That way, there are two people loving you instead of only one! This is actually a way of increasing self love; even though uncomfortable at times, you still are winning at loving. There is satisfaction and joy in supporting each other.

Love expresses at every level of existence. Freely loving others, groups, a "good cause," principles and the world keeps the flow moving toward wholeness. Love leads your life and makes the world go 'round. Love is caring: caring for oneself; caring for someone else; caring for family or groups; caring for spiritual purposes; caring for our world. Whatever you do you are caring for yourself or for another. Most individuals are not short of love, only on the ability to express love in a mature way.

If you could accept the possibility of love being present in every situation, you could identify the positive intent behind everyone's behavior. You then could speak to a person's listening by communicating on a level that would bring out the reality - the *truth* of the matter! Love is patient, understanding and connects us to each other in ONENESS — Children of the same Spirit and heirs of the same birthright.

> *"I look with caring eyes and see the love that is in, around, and through all, rejoicing - all is love!"*

355

5. Unconditional Love Is the Essence of Who We Are

Unconditional love is the very essence of spirit and can only be experienced in the moment (now, and now, and now). Like "coming home," we experience our full potential of loving without judgment. It involves an experience of complete honesty and purity, as if all things were understandable. It is easier to say what unconditional love isn't, than to say what it is, because it is a happening. It is not a feeling, but an experience of wholeness, harmlessness and peace. Maybe it's what fills space!

Judgment blocks spontaneous love from taking place. As you judge others, you more severely judge yourself and vice versa. Self-judgment can be masked with denial and projected onto others as "unacceptable behavior." This takes the form of criticism and blame. What is feared or unforgiven in yourself is what you will find the most difficult to forgive in others. When you are willing to love and accept yourself the way you are, you will more easily love others as they are. The problem is that people use criticism and blame as a motivator to get what they want, not realizing they are giving up the most precious gift of all - ultimate happiness and joy.

The consequence for not knowing that you **are** unconditional love creates the bondage to BECOME what you already are! You can never do that! To even try creates struggle. Fear and insecurity take the place of the peaceful state of unconditional love.

Someone once asked me how to find unconditional love. I told her that it could not be found, it was who she was, just express it! She did not like my answer. Therefore, I told her to just practice some old fashioned conditional love and she would one day discover it. "There are none so blind as those who will not see."

"There are reasons or results, and reasons don't count," is one of my favorite sayings. If you believe that you cannot love unconditionally, you can't. In fact, you will be able to come up with all kinds of proof that you can't. We have all been trained and programmed to fear, not love. We are all programmed to need a reason to do what we do. Guess what? You don't need a reason. You can choose to love unconditionally any moment you want.

You can choose to give out love, acceptance and understanding, no matter what the circumstances. You reap the glorious benefit of living in unconditional love when you accept the unacceptable, love the unlovable and stop worrying about what other people think. Stop being so logical and just choose to love everyone, even if they don't seem to like you. There is something to love about everyone. Unconditional love is often not comfortable, yet it is wonderful. Our mind is conditional and suspicious of any uncomfortable experience.

Instead of collecting reasons why a person is unlovable, choose to love and accept them anyway. Bless everyone you meet. Seek to share the love you are freely and openly. You can choose to love at any moment. You can choose to look through another person's eyes or

357

through their heart and understand why they are as they are. A beautiful description of unconditional love is given in I Corinthians 13, where this godly love believes, hopes, endures and bears ALL things. "Love never fails."

> *"I accept myself as I am, therefore I accept you also, unconditionally — and am open to further understanding."*

6.   Every Act Is an Act of Love, Either Giving it or Trying to Get it

Because there is a *positive intention* behind every action, from the very essence of our being, it is coming out of love. Love is behind every act, no matter how immaturely that love is expressed at the time.

Some exceptions are acts that stem from drugged, deranged, and *"possessed"* states when the mind is out of control. When the normal functioning of the mind is interfered with, it is difficult to trace the positive intent and the love beneath it. Yet even these dysfunctional states were originally chosen out of a *positive intent* (usually to escape pain) and self-protective love.

It is our dual mind (conscious and subconscious) that underlines interprets our fundamentally loving intention and sends it out through the only method it can, its own judgments and beliefs. Maybe you can even create being treated a certain way so you can be right! For example: When you hold a belief that "you are not enough," you attract others to let you be right about it. They will remind you that you aren't!

The consequences for not being aware of this Principle will get you into problems in relationships, as the mind would rather be right than happy. When you believe that someone deliberately wants to hurt you, you cause upsets in your life. The other person was acting out of some kind of love, and not getting any credit for it. This moves to arguing and complaining, which destroys relating.

Experiment with the possibility that you can come to the common denominator of your actions - the bottom line of intention. Go back in time and re-look at a regretful situation. Now, go to right before that situation happened. What was your positive intent to do what you did? Even though you can change your mind soon afterward, at the moment you did what you did, you had a positive intent to give or receive love. Notice what changed your mind? Everyone has a positive intent behind what they do. Your job is to understand what that is, so you can connect with the love that's there, rather than stew in the effects of it.

Explore the possibility that you are a *being* of love; therefore, so are others. Notice how you desire love, peace and harmony in your life and in the lives of those around you. So do others! Note how much love is at the basis of your every action, either for yourself or others. As you come to the threshold of life - celebrate that every act is an act of love!

*"My every act surrenders to the conscious
expression of love."*

7. There Is No Evil Act, Though the Result Can Appear to Be

This principle extends to you a possibility that acts themselves cannot be judged fairly from their appearances, for every act originates in love. This is not to say evil does not exist. Rather, it is to say that there is always a positive intent present in each situation. You may get a surprise when the deepest motivations are known. Think of the story in Book One, about the person in the convertible, who had his hood smashed in with a rock. He judged the act as evil until he saw the truth. Maybe every act could be done in the proper circumstances and lose its judgment of evil.

The Greek word for sin is "missing the mark." This intimates the aim was to be on target. You cannot miss a mark unless you are aiming. Acts are like arrows of the mind aiming to hit its programmed target - *to be right, proper and justified.* It is the mind's way of functioning. The mind must be right to survive.

At Christ's crucifixion, he said, "Father, forgive them for they know not what they do." Jesus knew the people were aiming to be on target; and they missed the mark! They really didn't know what they were doing. They thought he was an imposter and should be killed! Is this not why he could so readily forgive? Open to the possibility that everyone is trying to hit the mark and see what happens to your vision.

Not understanding this Principle causes unnecessary stress and anxiety. Anger builds as you judge wrongly. You will pay for the consequences for holding on to your logical belief that people *"know what's right, and do wrong anyway!"* It is simply not true!

The pain that comes from not understanding this Principle is great. The diseases that are created out of anger, resentment and hate are astonishing. Problems with the male and female organs are a result of unforgiveness with an intimate partner. More murders are committed within families, especially mates, than strangers. Understanding is the mind's way of experiencing unconditional love. The psychological definition for unconditional love is: "Before anyone can say or do anything, they first (in that moment) must feel it is right, proper, or justified" or it cannot happen.

Mature love understands that your mate is not seeking to hurt you. Therefore, you can ask the necessary questions to understand the positive intent behind the behavior. All are aiming for the bull's eye, yet sometimes miss the mark. Reactionary behavior is the result. And all reactionary behavior is built upon fear. Your mind is only interested in being comfortable. Understanding is the key.

The admonition to *"do good to those who hurt you,"* is sound advice. This advice boggles the mind, which cannot justify returning kindness for hurt. Though, if you could, to whom would you want to express it? Try it! The sooner you stop judging the act and go behind it to understand the intent, the sooner you will resolve your problems and create truly loving relationships. You then can be free to share your love in a mature way.

"I do not judge the outer appearance, but quickly go where truth is found."

8. There Are No Victims!

This is a well argued paradox. You can choose to use this stance as a place of empowerment to resolve problems. It allows you to conceive new possibilities of cause. When you stop looking for someone or something to blame, you look inside and find the real cause. There is always a perpetration behind every problem, a lie that hides the truth. Acknowledging that you are not a victim is a way for you to take responsibility for what you create in your world. If you own it, you can heal it. Some say they can't help being the way they are because of their parents. What if you even chose your PARENTS?

When going into the subconscious mind during case after case of molestations, dysfunctional behaviors and early childhood wounds, I find no victims. Instead I find people acting very immaturely out of love and fear. Generational patterns develop as immature patterns of loving are passed to the following generation.

If you support the belief that "we are all victims," life becomes a fearful event, never knowing when an illness or disaster may strike. Life becomes a constant threat with victim programming, and does not serve wellness.

I am not asking you to believe this, only to experiment with the possibility, as your mind will quickly reject it. Just own up to whatever is going on in your life and pretend you chose it. See what happens to the mind. The mind can help you resolve problems best when it takes responsibility for those problems (being at cause) and looks within itself for answers. Then your mind will do everything it can to make things better again.

Ultimately, we are all victims of the earth, weather, people, government, economy, our thoughts, etc., or are we? Here again you face a decision of TRUST. Are you going to trust Spirit to bring you to the exact experience to help you learn your lessons for growth? I am happy to know I am never subjected to any circumstance I do not have the power to overcome and benefit by! Life is ever expanding my love and trust, bringing constant benefits.

"I am not a victim! I accept 'what is' and create positive results in my life."

9. Behind Every Feeling and Action Is a Positive Intent

Behind every action is a POSITIVE INTENTION that wants to be right or do right, however that shows up. When you see what that is, you will be a master communicator. You can then communicate directly to the source where problems can be resolved. Experiment with the possibility that behind every action is a positive intent.

363

Speaking to the positive intent, you discover intimate communication and heart to heart connection.

Judgment comes from looking at the outward behavior. Through your eyes you see behavior which the mind automatically processes through its memory banks and evaluates. You process information in at least two ways: how you *think* about it and how you *feel* about it. This processing is limited.

Unless you look to other means of understanding, you are only in touch with outward appearances. Powerful communication goes to the intention behind the action. What you see begins with an intention, then goes through the mind's programming out into the world of action. It is the action you end up seeing, and that action may not be expressed very maturely, because of the programming.

By living from the notion that there is a positive intent behind every act and every feeling, you can make some amazing discoveries. Unwillingness to open to this perspective will interfere with your ability to relate maturely with others. Inside each person is the knowing that behind whatever they are doing is a positive intent. Your job, as a master communicator, is to understand what that intent is. Listen to a child speak; their questioning mind can lead you to further understanding. They are always open to share what **they** want.

When you do not know why you or someone else is acting or feeling a certain way, look for the positive intent. You will understand yourself and others much clearer if you ask the following questions:

1. What do I really want to express?
2. What are you wanting to express?
3. What is my positive intent in expressing it?
4. What is your positive intent?
5. Why am I thinking and feeling this way?
6. Why are you thinking and feeling this way?

Until your own intention is clear, it is unlikely you will express it maturely. Unnecessary upsets occur because the positive intent behind the behavior was never revealed. A common ground for communication must be established. Sharing how you feel and asking for what you want is the basis for clear communication, not who's right. Understanding the positive intent gets you to where you want to go much faster.

Feelings are not right or wrong, good or bad. Feelings are just the way you feel. Sharing them will help you make a trail to the positive intent and clarify your wants. Practice sharing how you feel and ask others to do the same. Without sharing feelings you will find communication close to impossible. "Most people don't communicate, they just keep talking."

"I am clear on my intentions and readily see the positive intentions of others, as I open my heart in love."

10. Before Anyone Can Say or Do Anything, They First must Feel it Is Right, Proper or Justified

In reviewing your life, everything you ever said or did was thought to be right, proper or justified in that moment of doing it. Perhaps five minutes later a different judgment was made, but in that moment you acted on what you thought to be right or justified. Your mind must feel right, proper or justified to survive. Even prisoners I interviewed justified themselves with a logical reason at the moment of each crime. Many of them were <u>still</u> justifying their crime.

The consequences for avoiding this Principle is that you will be affected emotionally, socially and spiritually. You cannot carry the belief that "people know what's right and do wrong anyway" and live a nonjudgmental life. Understanding this Principle will give you a great benefit in letting go of judging and living by the spirit. Powerful relationships form through understanding this Principle. It is not a "cop out," only humbling to your mind.

Every Principle may have an exception. When the mind is not under self-control because of drugs, compulsive addictions or entities, it may lose its innate drive to do what is right, proper or justified. The mind's normal functioning may become dulled and insensitive to rational behavior. Usually the mind serves us well, making a wonderful servant.

Conflicts arise in relationships because each person's mind needs to be right. So, if your mind needs to be right for its survival, can you see how important it is to acknowledge this for others and give them the same opportunity? Allowing others to "be right" for even a few moments will allow you to look through their eyes and understand their viewpoint. This can bring deep understanding, loving acceptance and valuable healing.

> *"I am understanding with others and willing to look at situations through their eyes."*

11. All Things Work for Good and Work a Benefit

It encourages me to know that no matter what, there is a benefit in every situation! This Principle has made the biggest single difference in my areas of stress to transform them into areas of joy. Someone once said, "God turns lemons into lemonade."

I have experienced severe disappointments changed into blessings. Acknowledging that an unknown benefit is soon to be disclosed, begins the healing process. This *knowing* motivates me to stay in a positive attitude. Knowing that all is well and ultimately beneficial is comforting to my soul. I love this knowing!

The consequence for not seeing a benefit in all things can lead you into worry and fear. Worry affects the pancreas, which produces insulin to maintain a normal blood sugar. The pancreas also produces enzymes for the second stage of digestion. We are living in a time when

367

very few people are living worry free lives. Notice how cancer, diabetes and hypoglycemia have skyrocketed. Between refined sugar, undigested protein and worry, any pancreas would have a difficult time.

The most frightening threshhold to pass through is the unknown. When you know there is a benefit beyond every experience you can lighten up about your life. Maybe, that is what "enlightenment" is all about - getting lighter!

This axiom focuses my attention on the answer, instead of the problem. Looking for the benefit helps me take responsibility for what is going on in my life. It lightens my attitude and gives me space to go on and experiment with Life in a meaningful way.

When in a difficult situation, I mentally list all the possible benefits and release the emotional hold, trusting that all will work for good. This usually clears my path to discovering that what I thought was a disaster is actually a blessing. My mind then opens to many possibilities for using the situation to give thanks. Sometimes, I start giving thanks before I even know what the benefit is, just on faith. It keeps me in a GREAT ATTITUDE as I re-member, "**All** things work for good for those who love the Lord..."

"I look for the benefit in each situation."

12. Wholeness and Happiness Is Everyone's Birthright

We are whole, created in the image of God. A happy life is everyone's birthright. The body/mind makes automatic adjustments to keep us in comfort and health. This is why the body is a valuable barometer. Sickness may be the result of the body's attempt to keep us in balance. For example: When there are high levels of toxins (poisons) in the body, the body may wall them off, so they will not harm an organ. The body makes adjustments to keep us alive, whole and in balance.

You can determine what is out of balance inwardly by how it shows up outwardly in the body. I notice my sinuses become congested when I feel sorry for myself. When I focus on gratitude they clear right up. Our bodies are constantly giving us messages, which I call "wake-up" calls, to keep us in balance. Even accidents are "wake-up" calls. All of this shows how our main purpose is to live a spiritual life of love, kindness and happiness.

When you are not experiencing a fullness of joy, ask yourself, "Am I listening to my inner guidance and taking care of my emotional and spiritual well-being?" You may find that you are not living out of your *divine purpose*. You may have forgotten that you are not on this planet by accident, but by divine design to fulfill a *joyous purpose!* "We are not human beings having a spiritual experience, but are spiritual beings having a human experience!"

"I am grateful to be whole in body, mind, and spirit."

13. The Only Unhappiness Is the <u>Need</u> to Be Happy

Unhappiness arises out of feeling that something is missing. It is the normal reaction of the mind to tell us when we are not appreciating something about our life, our circumstances or another person. As soon as we acknowledge that we forgot to love, appreciate, etc., and accept what is going on in that moment, we can go back into happiness again.

Because the mind functions on needing more — better — different, it will keep wanting more love, better love, or a different kind of love. Watch your mind. It can never be satisfied. This "NEEDY" feeling or belief keeps you moving and changing, but with a price to pay.

Negative emotional patterns of behavior are developed through constantly comparing what is to what "should be." Always *looking* for happiness creates its own unhappiness, as happiness can never be found outside of one's self. I **am** happy, therefore, I **am** ok! Unhappiness can be used by the mind as a motivator to make you do what it feels must be done to be a success. Since happiness gives you a sense of success, the mind fears you will not deserve being successful. And the vicious cycle continues. Happiness is only found within, now.

"Happiness fills my heart, therefore I am a success!"

14. To the Degree That We Experience Pain, Sadness or Disappointment, Is to That Degree We Expand Our Peace, Love, Joy

"The deeper that sorrow carves into
your being, the more joy you can contain."
Kahil Gibran

Everything in Life is in balance like a pendulum. To the degree that you suffer, is to the degree that you can appreciate what being free of that suffering is like. For instance, a felon, who has been locked up for a time, truly knows and appreciates what it is to be free!

Most people have experienced enough pain, so what about exploring its opposite? How much joy can you contain? What are you willing to experiment with? What if you woke up each day grateful to be alive? What if you really appreciated your relationships? Experiment with creating heaven on earth for a month and see what happens. Where would you spend your time, what would you be doing, with whom would you do it, and how would you feel?

It's time for your pain to end. God wants you to notice that you have suffered enough. If you had children, wouldn't you want them to live in joy? Maybe it's time to stop resisting pain and disharmony, appreciate the benefits obtained and move on to exploring heavenly happiness!

"I appreciate what was, accept what is, and am open to embrace my full potential of love and joy!"

15. Gratitude Is the Healing Energy of the Body, You Can Choose at Any Moment

I experimented with gratitude, "Giving thanks in *all* things." I found it to be one of the greatest principles in living a joyous life and speeding up the process of healing. I found when I chose to accept and be glad about whatever was going on, I could see the benefit quickly. This changed my attitude and gave me a sense of being responsible for my life. By choosing to be greatful in any situation, I found the results I was looking for. I invite you also to experiment. You will find there is always something to appreciate in every moment.

Upsets will happen, but we do not have to stay in the upset. We have the power of CHOICE! We can choose at any moment to appreciate what is going well and look for the benefit in the areas of uncertainty.

Gratitude is having a GREAT ATTITUDE and regenerates the healing powers of the body.

Our bodies can regenerate themselves at a startling rate if given the chance. Sinuses can clear up in a matter of minutes, growths can disappear in a matter of hours. What are you willing to experiment with? You have nothing to loose and the consequences are high. Without gratitude and appreciation your life is not worth living. Your energy is low and friends are few. Life looses its zest and value. No one wants to be around a "bad attitude."

Stop right now, take a big breath and feel gratitude flow through your body. Think of all the things you are grateful for. Think of how much you appreciate being alive! Smile and be grateful! Allow gratitude to grow in you until you recognize feelings of praise. Praise is a celestial form of gratitude. I love to stop many times during a day, appreciate the beauty, and say, "Thank you God for this beautiful earth."

"My body heals and my mind transforms
as my spirit rejoices in gratitude!"

16. We All Have a Divine Purpose for Living

Live out of the possibility your birth on earth was no accident, but by divine intent! We ALL have a divine purpose, whether realized or not.

When I say "divine purpose," I mean special godly qualities — making our world a better place in which to live. A divine purpose is: <u>An ongoing event that always has to do with others</u>. All are uniquely created with talents and gifts to contribute in a special way. All have different gifts to share. We were not placed on an island to be alone, but with people.

A purpose is a state of living purposefully.

The consequence of avoiding your divine purpose is that your aliveness is affected. Monotony and boredom affects your energy level. Your immune system requires a happy life to function in its full potential. Unless you are experiencing a purpose for living, your health can be threatened and a part of you can lose its will to live.

Abraham Maslow's research on the levels of human need and development concludes that money only initially motivates us. Unless there is a spiritual benefit to your career, you experience lack or unfulfillment. Living in your purpose induces the highest energy level and greatest health. Many hidden death wishes are because of not having a genuine purpose to live!

You can choose to live your purpose at any time and in any place by expressing your divine qualities that make a difference in people's lives. Each quality is a way of loving: Compassion, understanding, intimate sharing, giving a listening ear, friendliness, empowering others to succeed, easily forgiving others, etc. The list goes on. How you choose to manifest your purpose in the world is up to you. You can choose a career which allows the fulfilling of your purpose easier. Books have now been written on how to succeed at the thing you love to do most. Explore living purposefully.

*"My health and happiness increases
through living my divine purpose."*

17. The Greatest Risk of All in Life Is Not Risking

The adage, "Nothing ventured, nothing gained" still holds true. Some people die prematurely because they are so miserable in their life and can't see leaving any other way. It may be that *not* risking is the riskiest thing of all. Life can take on new meaning and enthusiasm when you involve yourself in what you love the most. It's wonderful to wake up in the morning, being enthused about life!

Opening your heart in an intimate relationship is risking possible hurt or disappointment. Not risking is much worse. You could be risking your greatest possible joy by not opening your heart and sharing your feelings intimately. Your fear is only a temporary twinge, heavy feeling, queasy sensation, lightheadedness, warm temperature rise, etc. Most fears are illusions manufactured by the mind to keep you safe and comfortable.

When you do not let go of an unfulfilling job because you are afraid you cannot "make it" doing what you love to do, you risk not only your joy in life, but your health too. Many job injuries occur with people who cannot say: "I don't want to work here anymore." Therefore, they create a work injury or illness that does not allow them to stay on the job.

375

Sickness and hardships occur when you are not true to yourself in a spiritual and an emotional way. Living your life purpose can bring you happiness, satisfaction and a sense of value. Be courageous! Risk more (guided by Spirit that is)!

> *"I listen to the calling in my heart*
> *and bravely follow my dreams!"*

18. The Mind Functions from A False Purpose for Living – To Be Non-disturbed

Our minds are programmed to help us survive, mentally, emotionally, and physically. To survive mentally the mind must be right; emotionally, it must be accepted; and physically, it must make adjustments to keep life flowing and keep us safe from pain or harm. Therefore, survival is of the greatest importance to the mind, rather than the quality of our lives. This is why the mind would rather be right than happy. It would rather be safe than risk the discomfort of change.

At birth we experience pain for the first time. A decision is made on a subconscious level that "pain is bad and comfort is good and the purpose of living is to be non-disturbed." See *A New Day In Healing, Chapter Six.* Though helpful for survival, this programming is not encouraging for our happiness and joy. In fact, it is during the uncomfortable times that we learn and grow the most.

Survival programming is valuable, for it protects us

from self-destruction. So, let's appreciate it! When we realize everyone is programmed this way, we can have more empathy for people wanting to take the easy way out. We can support each other to make the best choice.

Not understanding how our minds work can cause premature judging that creates upsets in our lives. Unresolved upsets are at the foundation of most people's problems. In every case of chronic illness I find buried unresolved hurts from the past. People hide their feelings and do not speak out for what they want.

This "NEED FOR COMFORT" programming makes you a victim of you own mind. Understanding that the mind is there to serve you, not direct your life, can be a valuable aid in taking charge of your life as well as your health. When you are willing to go beyond comfort to higher purposes you experience mastery.

"I am patient and respond lovingly to people
for I understand the mind's programming."

19. We Are Not Minds, We Are Spirit.

We are PRESENT time human BEINGS created in the image of God, far more than PAST time programming (a mind). We are present time *Beings* with an incredibly capable mind to serve us.

We HAVE a mind; so are not what we have. Our mind is made of the sum total of all of our past experiences, including all our thoughts and feelings. The mind is programming like the software of a computer.

Every experience ever recorded is held in our mind, including how we THINK and how we FEEL about it. All activities and incidents go into our memory banks. Even though it may be difficult to separate yourself, you are DISTINCT from your mind.

Your mind only functions in the past or future, while you (spirit) function only in the present, NOW. You are the OBSERVER of your programming.

Problems arise when you forget **who** you are (and who *they* are) and *react* from your programming, instead of functioning from spirit. Spirit always wants to treat others fairly, and is open to learn what that looks like. Self-righteousness is the result of a closed unyielding mind taking control. Conflict occurs when you refuse to listen to and trust spirit, letting doubt and fear take control.

Explore the conversation in your mind! Is it upbeat, fascinating or discouraging? Are you happy to be alive? Thoughts are constantly being spoken inside your head. This inner conversation is your constant ally or antagonist. Though you are not your busy mind, you are the watcher WHO is listening to the chatter. You have the power to choose which thoughts to follow or discard. You have the power to change your thoughts. As you change your thoughts your feelings change also. You write the script, direct the show and hire the actors on your stage. If you don't like it, change it.

You can CHOOSE what serves in this moment. My invitation to you is to live in the NOW (in the spirit), and observe your mind. Be aware of how you are functioning at any time. As your judgmental mind renews, you enjoy your full potential of joy and happiness. When you live in the NOW, time seems to stand still. Each moment transcends time, aging, judgment and sorrow.

When living from spirit and not programmed response, you are fully present to this moment, allowing a fresh choice. Boredom disappears. The present moment circumstances are just enough different that the past has little or no relativity to it. Your programming may try to label your experience and hook it up with the past. No! Choose newly this moment what serves best, making a choice from new understanding under spirit's guidance. You are not your mind. Mind is a servant to spirit, making your life worthwhile. I surely wouldn't want to be without it!

> *"I have dominion over my mind, and source my life anew each moment."*

20. Our Word Is Powerful

You were made in the image of God and have been promised dominion over the earth! You can take authority over unwanted doubts, fears and inflammation in your body through speaking the "word of faith." You can bind and command virus, inflammation, etc. to leave. You can immediately change energy by declaring it so. The power of prayer avails much and is scientifically sound.

379

Through MRT you can demonstrate how quickly the body responds to command. You can just think of a negative thought and your muscle will go weak. You can think or speak a word of love and cause a weak part of your body to test strong. How you think affects the strength of your body and its ultimate well-being.

You can overcome (oppressive) interferences by speaking them away, as in *Chapter Fifteen* of this text. Oppressive energies can attach to the body's aura (electrical field) and increase the magnitude of a problem. Negative energy forms take on the vibration of the problem and accentuate it. Every disease may have a counterpart "thought form." You can take authority over these energy forms, bind them and take them out and away from your body because your WORD is powerful! You can also speak the word of healing over them and change them into complementary energy in the Universe.

"I am Spirit, therefore my Word is powerful."

21. Outside of the States of Peace, Love and Joy, a Perpetration Is Attached

A perpetration is something you believe is true, that isn't, a self-deception or lie. It might be something you think you should do that you don't, causing automatic guilt. Whichever way it shows up, you are left with negative emotions. My own research brought me to discover that whenever I had a feeling outside of a peaceful state, I was in a perpetration. I used this discovery to trace each negative reaction back to its origin to find the cause. I was amazed to find a perpetration was always lurking there.

Peace, love and joy are the natural states of our spiritual essence. I differentiate between Spirit of God with a capitol "S" and our spirit with a small "s," not that there is a separation, but a distinction. Our spirit is of the same essence as God's. When we live, move, function from our divine essence, which is a "NOW" experience, we are living from the "fruits" of the Spirit: Love, joy, peace, patience, kindness, goodness, faithfulness, gentleness and self-control. When functioning from our minds, we will usually find ourselves "running from" a discomfort, as the mind operates from fear.

The mind judges and resists every uncomfortable feeling, not understanding our true purpose. This kind of programming creates emotional demands that are difficult, if not impossible, to satisfy. Then to make matters worse, the mind is never satisfied, because it wants more, better and different.

Perpetrations can serve us by letting us know if we are functioning in the spirit or stuck in our fearful minds. In this way we are reminded to surrender to Spirit! By surrendering to Spirit, we stop being pulled into a negative judgmental way of being to live a transformed life.

So anytime you feel less than peace or happiness, **look** for the justification with a perpetration attached! As soon as you *see* the truth, you are set free! The good news is that only you can *see* for yourself, no one can see for you.

"I examine myself when I am not happy and uncover the perpetration that would hold me bound, thus releasing peace and joy."

22. Discernment Is of the Spirit. Judging Is from the Mind and Causes Perpetrations to Form

Discernment is a NOW experience, a *gift* from the Spirit. When you go into silence, listen to the Spirit within and surrender to the guidance of that inner voice, and you will stay out of the perpetrations of the mind.

Perpetrations form from the mind's judging (drawing a conclusion before all the evidence is in). When the mind becomes defensive to justify thoughts or actions, it is a sign there is a perpetration attached. As an example: "Dad hit me, so I *know* he doesn't love me." A false assumption is made out of being hit: "I am not loved" the mind shouts. When a decision is made with intense emotion attached, it CREATES A PATTERN from that time forth. The mind automatically creates experiences to prove that the assumption is true. "I knew Dad didn't care because..." These are justifications. One after another are created and projected onto others for the mind to prove it's right. Consequently, connectedness ends!

You can go beyond this negative repetitious cycle by STOPPING judgment. This begins with being compassionate with yourself, understanding it is not you; it is your early childhood programming. Will directs your life, mind carries out the instructions through your body, all to assist you to survive. Therefore, as you surrender your *will* to God's Will, listening to the inner voice of Spirit, you are able to see clearly and make decisions that bring happiness and success. This knowing can keep you out of judging and in a great attitude!

"I let go of judgments and rejoice in the discerning of truth, which I clearly see!"

23. The Truth Shall Set You Free

On a physical level, the truth is learned. On a mental level, the truth is discovered. On a spiritual level, the truth is created. On all levels of expression, truth sets us free.

Truth, as I am using the term, means "what is so." Seeing "what is so" is seeing clearly. It is being able to go beyond the surface confusion of appearances and expose the love that is there. Remember the story of the man who judged the boy who threw the rock at his car. His anger and hate changed to compassion as soon as he saw "the truth."

Pain and sorrow are a result of not knowing "the truth." Truth goes beyond the limitations of the mind into the eternal realms of spiritual evolution and growth. If you could see clearly, you would see the presence of love and beauty. The next time you feel sad or lonely, ask yourself: "What untruth am I believing to support my

feeling this way? What is the eternal truth involved?"
You also might ask yourself, "What is my payoff for
staying in this negative feeling?"

*"I check my emotions and reserve my judgment,
knowing that only the truth will set me free!"*

24. I Am 100 Percent Responsible for My Experience of You - You Are 100 Percent Responsible for Your Experience of Me

You can only see with your own eyes through your
own programming. What you see is not simply an account
of what is. It is a filtered perception of what you subconsciously believe. It is more a "looking for" than a "looking at."

Everyone sees through their individual experience,
tainted by subconscious beliefs. Thus, what you actually
end up seeing is what your subconscious programming is
looking for. When you hold anger inside, you see others
as angry people. If you fuss over everything, you may act
intolerant of unorganized people. Others are like mirrors
of your own programming. Whatever it is that you do not
accept in others is exactly what you do not accept in yourself. When you do not allow yourself to be a certain way,
such as sloppy, you certainly cannot allow this same behavior in someone else. This is why you are 100% responsible for how you see others to be. You can only see
"out there" what you can relate to inside.

When an artist looks at a tree, many shades of green come into view. The non-artist sees only one or two shades. Your ability to identify distinctions in life increases as you quietly observe, connect with, and express. In a similar way, as you renew your mind to express more positive aspects, you will notice more people also living out of that same place. Notice how when you buy a new car, how many of them are on the road that you didn't notice before.

This principle can work a great benefit for you. THE MORE YOU ACCEPT OF YOURSELF THE MORE LIKABLE EVERYONE ELSE WILL BE! You can be your own teacher by noticing what it is in others that really bothers you and clear those issues in your own life. If this Principle is difficult for you, just pretend that you are responsible for how others show up in your life and you will receive a great benefit, and so will they. You will find what you are looking for!

"I appreciate being responsible for how I create you to show up in my life."

25. We Create Our Own World

By all means, don't make a belief of this; only experiment with it! I look at myself as a co-creator with Spirit. To create means to "bring into being." Create can also mean organizing already existing matter into something new.

Sometimes when I refer to "we," I am actually referring to "me" as a plural being. I notice that many times my mind thinks it is me, so do my feelings and my body. So here we have three: A mind that wants to keep me right, proper or justified; feelings that want acceptance; and a body that wants to be protected from pain and physical discomfort. And then there is ME! I am the one who makes the CHOICES of what I want my life to be.

You create your life by the choices you make. If it's difficult owning up to what you are creating, at least experiment by pretending (you are creating it). Pretend you are creating who I am to you! Since you can only see through your eyes, you create your experience of me. I create my experience of you; and you concurrently are creating who I am to you. The mind is powerful enough to focus on what it believes to such an extent it can only see just that. You experience life in two major ways:

1. Being at CAUSE.
2. Being at the EFFECT.

The consequences of living your life at the effect of how everyone else acts is painful. Helplessness and depression are the result. This leads to many problems with the nervous system, bones, sinuses, and can be the foundation of many physical ailments. Only when you get a sense of the reality of how you create your world, do you experience the empowerment you deserve. You are not a victim of your world, you are in charge!

If you really did create your own world, what would you do differently? Allow your creativity to explore many dimensions of possibility. Experiment with the possibility that you are at cause and allow yourself to fulfill your dream!

"I enjoy creating my world."

26. Choice Comes from the Spirit, as Our Birthright - Our Free Will

The freedom to make our own choices is one of our greatest gifts as human beings. Knowing that no one can control us is empowering. Only we can control ourselves. No one can think for us, eat for us, speak for us, etc. This is not to say there will not be times of wishing we could control another person. It just means that it is impossible! And it can be very frustrating even to try.

A true choice requires at least two different possibilities; otherwise, choice is not present. Choice is not the neediness of the mind that says, "I need this or I must have that," but consciously picking a direction of action. To experience making a true choice, <u>YOU MAKE IT UP</u>! It is not dependent upon neediness. Neediness is a product of your mind, not the consciousness of choice.

Free will is not license. It is not the permission to do anything we want, anytime we want; if that doing would hurt another human being. Free will enables us to respond to life in our own unique way. We can choose to, or choose not to, at any time. Living in maturity means living with the knowing that only we can respond for ourselves, hence: "Response ability." Free will supports our winning and growing to be all that we CHOOSE to be.

> *"I appreciate choosing what my life will be and owning the outcome."*

27. We Live in What We Radiate

We radiate out from the very center of our being. Whatever thoughts we focus on brings up feelings from the subconscious mind. Those feelings emit energy and make up the energy in and around us. We actually live in that energy field. We breathe back its very substance. People near us are affected by the energy we put out. Someone once said that the only thing more contageous than enthusiasm is unenthusiasm. Although we are affected by the energy around us, we can only feel our response to it, not the energy itself. We cannot feel anything outside of ourselves. I love what Alexander Lowen, M.D. said:

"It is an axiom of bioenergetic analysis that what a person really feels is his body. He cannot feel the environment except through its action upon his body. He feels how his body reacts to stimuli proceeding from the environment, and then he projects this feeling on the stimuli. Thus when I sense that your hand is warm as it rests upon my arm, what I feel is the warmth in my arm that is produced by your hand. All feelings are body perceptions. If

a person's body does not respond to the environment, he feels nothing. "[25]

Do you want to live in love? Then send out love. Do you want to live in gratitude? Then send it out! Whatever you want your life to be about is the key to give away.

Love flows from within outward and through you to others. <u>You can only experience love as you send it out</u>. Think of a time when you loved someone intensely, but they didn't like you. Remember how your heart would thump at the very thought of them? You really experienced love. Now think of a time when someone loved you and you didn't care for them. In fact, it repulsed you when they came around. Did you feel all that love coming toward you? Of course you didn't! You only felt the repulsion (what you were sending out)!

Not understanding and applying this Principle can lead to continual frustration, always looking to receive something that can never be experienced. What an awful way to lead a life! No wonder the world is filled with disappointment and sorrow. Few people realize that they live in what they radiate. Sharing this Principle with all you meet can create a wonderful world of responsible joy.

> *"Love and appreciation multiplies in me as I live in what I send out."*

---

[25]From Biology of the Mind/Body, Dept. Of Behavioral Biology, University of California, Davis, Jim Polidora, Instructor.

28. Separation Is an Illusion Calling Us to Live Joyfully

We are constantly experiencing oneness or separation. We can choose to express the oneness of love and peace that blesses our lives and those around us or observe life as separate. Seeing through spiritual eyes, all is part of one big whole. To the mind everything is separate. This is fine, as we are able to experience the paradox of life - all separate and all one. One way of seeing is not better than the other, only more enjoyable. Each viewpoint has its benefit.

Separateness may have consequences of *feelings* of abandonment, rejection and sorrow, or it may give the experience of independence and freedom. You can always tell if a perpetration is attached because of the way you *feel* about it. Awareness of your feelings will support you.

When in wholeness and truth, your vision is clear. Personal empowerment comes from the awareness that we are one. No threat there! Could all things be part of a great whole? The very patterns of life show up in the macro universe, as well as in the microscope. Energy is made of atoms. Atoms are the same, whether in one form or another, except for the number of protons, neutrons and electrons circling around the nucleus. The same blueprint is found in all of life.

Looking at life as one big whole assists us in determining whether we are living out of the mind's <u>illusion</u> of separateness or whether we are living out of the <u>reality</u> of our existence. We could be a part of a great whole much larger than imagined. Could it be that we are connected at the most infinite level of all - Spirit?

When we heal ourselves could we be healing a part of the whole? As we transform our lives, could a part of the whole be transformed? Could separateness actually be an illusion of the mind? If so, separateness is a wonderful tool, letting you know in that moment, you are being driven by your mind, instead of spirit. Choosing to live in oneness will allow you to experience your mastership.

"Knowing we are One, lifts my love to joy!"

29. There Is No Such Thing as One Person Being Transformed Totally Until All Are

All people are of "one body." Just as one ailing part of our physical body affects another part, we may be influenced and affected by the other parts of humanity and not realize it. Our physical body is interdependent and interconnected with every other cell, as well as with our emotions, mind, and spirit.

It may be that we are similarly interdependent and interconnected with our global family as both science and psychology postulate. For example, one commonly accepted theory stipulates that suppressed emotions can go out sideways, seeking someone else to express through. The person who has a predisposition for expressing a particular emotion will be pushed into acting it out. Therefore, we do have an effect on each other.

391

With the unveiling of quantum physics, science has discovered that whatever information is in one cell of the body is in all the other cells! Being part of a WHOLE encourages me to support the world work better by being all I can be. Yet knowing that I can make a difference leaves no room for arrogance. Instead of creating false pride, it supports me to stop being a "respecter of persons," and allows me to be a respecter of all. What a wonderful world to live in with nobody being better than another. All, a part of one whole - different, yet one! "Ambitious pride (the need to be #1)" and the "need to control" are replaced with being fair, caring and sharing.

Living this Principle expands my mind beyond finite thinking to caring universally, regardless of a person's background, race or creed. It allows me to relax and enjoy the journey. We are all in this together! Let go of urgencies in your own personal growth, which create anxiety and competition. Remember, you live in what you radiate. Instead, be encouraged that whatever you accomplish profits all. This Principle *lightens* you up because THE ONLY PERSON TO FIX IS YOURSELF! And, of course, the only person you can fix is yourself! Progress in your own growth benefits the whole planet!

> *"I rejoice in the healing and advancement of all. As I grow, you benefit, as you grow I am blessed, for we are one."*

THE UNIVERSAL PRINCIPLES

1. The Only Constant in Life Is Change

2. Whatever We Resist Persists

3. The Flow of the Universe Is from Being — to Doing — to Having

4. Love Is the Basis of All Reality

5. Unconditional Love Is the Essence of Who We Are

6. Every Act Is an Act of Love, Either Giving it or Trying to Get it

7. There Is No Evil Act, Though the Result Can Appear to Be

8. There Are No Victims!

9. Behind Every Feeling and Action Is a Positive Intent

10. Before Anyone Can Say or Do Anything, They First must Feel it Is Right, Proper or Justified

11. All Things Work for Good and Work a Benefit

12. Wholeness and Happiness Is Everyone's Birthright

13. The Only Unhappiness Is the <u>Need</u> to Be Happy

14. To the Degree That We Experience Pain, Sadness or Disappointment, Is to That Degree We Expand Our Peace, Love and Joy

15. Gratitude Is the Healing Energy of the Body, You Can Choose at Any Moment

16. We All Have a Divine Purpose for Living

17. The Greatest Risk of All in Life Is Not Risking

18. The Mind Functions from a False Purpose for Living – to Be Non-disturbed

19. We Are Not Minds, We Are Spirits

20. Our Word Is Powerful

21. Outside of the States of Peace, Love and Joy, a Perpetration Is Attached

22. Discerning Is of the Spirit. Judging Is from the Mind and Causes Perpetrations to Form

23. Truth Sets You Free

24. I Am 100 Percent Responsible for My Experience of You and You Are 100 Percent Responsible for Your Experience of Me

25. We Create Our Own World

26. Choice Comes from the Spirit, It Is Our Birthright. It Is Our Free Will

27. We Live in What We Radiate

28. Separation Is an Illusion Calling Us to Live Joyfully

29. There Is No Such Thing as One Person Being Transformed Totally Until All Are

Participant's Page

1. For the next month study a Universal Principle each night. Write down any question or discussion you may want to have at a later time.

2. Experiment with the Principle for that day and record your experience. Share your experience with a friend.

3. Describe the difference between a belief about something versus your experience with it.

What Is a Health Facilitator?

A Health Facilitator is a Health Professional who is committed to supporting people to understand the **CAUSE** of their problem and how they can participate actively in their own healing process.

A Health Facilitator does not give advice, diagnose or prescribe, but rather teaches an individual how they can access information from their body through Muscle Response Testing (MRT) to uncover hidden information stored on a subconscious level. This information can lead to understanding **why** that ailment or problem exists.

A Health Facilitator encourages and supports people who have been overcome with hopelessness or helplessness by involving them in their healing at a causal level. This means that people can identify what specific emotions, patterns or beliefs are involved that are hampering the natural healing process.

Health Facilitators can educate a person on how their body works, how their mind works, and how the two interrelate. They understand the mental, physical, and spiritual laws behind problems and, therefore, assist people to understand what law they have broken, which has contributed to their problem.

Transformational healing is understood by a Health Facilitator, because it is the core aspect of health facilitation. Transformational healing is not about fixing problems, it is about holding life itself in a different paradigm - a paradigm of wholeness. It is about a "Spiritual Being having a human experience, rather than a human being having a spiritual experience."

Transformational healing draws one forward to living for something much larger than themselves - their Purpose! It is about "transforming one's life by the renewing of one's mind" and surrendering to Spirit. This heals not only at a physical level, but heals the soul and fulfills the purpose of one's being.

Health Facilitators support people to express their full potential and carry out their divine purpose in specific ways. They not only support people to heal themselves, but also to achieve goals such as: career changes, full potential relationships and spiritual alignment, no matter what their belief system. In fact, the healing process moves much more rapidly as people are moving toward meaningful goals. Many times boredom, emptiness, & disappointments contribute to their problem. By living out of a divine purpose one multiplies the healing energy of the body, which produces much faster results. Unless there is motivation to living, one begins to degenerate.

Health Facilitators can work with any health professional to support an individual to come to normal function and optimum well-being. They are able to identify when more specialized support is needed from another health professional, such as a medical doctor, osteopath, naturopath, acupuncturist, chiropractor, etc.

Being a Health Facilitator is a spiritual calling. Facilitators are aligned and living the laws of health themselves, so that they can share from their own experience. They are committed to "walking their talk" and living a high integrity life dedicated to serving God, living their divine purpose, and supporting others to do the same.

About the Author

Valerie Seeman Moreton is a graduate of the International College of Naturopathy and has been practicing wholistic healing, lecturing, and training students for over twenty years. She has intensively researched to find ways the body could heal itself through proper physical, mental and spiritual balance. In 1969, she began practicing as a nutritional consultant, while continuing her studies in pathology and bio-mechanics of the human body. Interning through her husband's medical/surgical practice gave her the opportunity to explore natural healing methods under orthodox supervision. As a result, the clinic's need for surgeries among its patients was greatly reduced and Valerie was proclaimed a "natural healer."

She expanded her studies of nutrition and herbology through Dr. Henry G. Bieler, M.D. and Dr. Bernard Jensen, N.D., D.C. By working with patients that the medical profession could no longer help, she was able to find additional ways to assist the body to heal itself. Next, she added the technology of "Creative Healing Massage" to alleviate pain and inflammation, then received her M.T. degree from Alpha Massage School, San Mateo, California in 1973.

Her studies with Stan Malstrom, N.D. and Dr. John Christopher motivated her to start lecturing on health, nutrition, herbology and Applied Kinesiology. In 1976, she became certified to teach the "Touch for Health" (TFH) Workshops. She taught hundreds of students TFH and advanced healing techniques on how to relieve pain, overcome allergies and release stress. She received special coaching from some of the most gifted people in Kinesiology, including; George Goodheart, D.C., John Thie, D.C.,

Sheldon Deal, D.C., Gordon Stokes, Daniel Whitesides, and Paul Dennison.

In 1978, Valerie founded Wholistic Health Education in El Dorado County, California. Through research with students and patients she developed many new methods for using Muscle Response Testing (MRT) to communicate with the body at much deeper levels and trace any problem to its source. In her continuing aim to integrate the body, mind and spirit in the healing process she became certified in One Brain, 1983; and Advanced One Brain, 1984, to work effectively with dyslexia and learning disabilities.

Valerie assisted in the development of the RFA (Relaxed Focused Attention) Process, a simplified method of helping to reprogram the subconscious mind to a perpetual positive attitude. The Process focused on clearing unwanted emotional blocks from early childhood by "seeing the truth" to be set free. The Kalos Process evolved out of the RFA Process, adding the "maturing of the mind" part.

With teaching as her major goal and joy, in 1986 she founded what is now Kalos Seminars International. With a commitment to healing and transformation, she has taught thousands of lay people and professionals how the body/mind works, how to relieve pain, how to overcome disease and how to take charge of their lives.

Glossary

Renewing Our Language

I am including words and phrases in this glossary to describe the distinctions from the usual way these terms have been used, to the way I am using them in this text. Some of the "new language" used herein has come from observing *how* we actually experience a situation, rather than the way we have been told *it is*. May the following expressions support your complete understanding and application of this work. Webster's Encyclopedic Dictionary (W.E.D.) is the source used to clarify certain descriptions.

Access — To uncover information at a cellular level, usually through the use of Muscle Response Testing (MRT).

Acupuncture — Chinese medical practice where needles are used to release pain or congestion in the body by way of acupuncture meridians located throughout the body.

Acupuncture meridians — Free-flowing colorless, non-cellular liquid which flows through independent vessels connecting the organs and muscles of the body. These vessels are considered a part of the body's electrical system and collapse upon death.

Affirmation — The assertion that something exists or is true. The act of affirming; not a declaration, which is the stating of a proclamation into being.

Agape — A Greek word meaning unconditional love, commonly referred to as "Godly love."

Age of Decision — The age when a decision is made with a perpetration attached, having consequences of preventing further maturity in that area.

Alignment — To connect, bring into harmony and balance.

Aliveness — A life filled with enthusiasm and purpose.

Applied Kinesiology — Kinesiology is the science dealing with the interrelationship of the physiological processes and anatomy of the human body with respect to motion; such as muscle movement in relationship to Muscle Response Testing. Applied refers to having a practical application of the information accessed. Therefore, Applied Kinesiology is the use of muscle movement, through MRT, to gain knowledge from the cells of the body.

Allopathy — Familiar Western medical treatment using drugs and/or surgery to preserve health or help the body recover from a disease, using agents producing effects different from those of the disease; as opposed to homeopathy which uses agents producing the same symptoms of the disease in a well person.

Attitude — The disposition of the mind, based upon deep feelings, tendencies or orientation. With feelings being dependent upon thoughts, a change in thinking affects the attitude. The clearer you see *reality*, the more positive the attitude becomes. See Prime Attitude Game.

Aura — An atmosphere like, electromagnetic field that emanates from a person, plant, animal or object.

Baptism of Fire — A spiritual purification process where one experiences a burning throughout one's body, combined with the experience of complete forgiveness, inner purity, joy, and unconditional, nonjudgmental love.

Being there — Attentive listening and compassionately interacting with someone when you are with them, as opposed to allowing the mind to wander and think about other things.

Bio-electrical computer — The brain and mind working together with the body's entire electrical and nervous system. With the body and brain being the hardware, the mind being the software of our bio-electrical computer to create the synergistic functioning of our body.

Brain Integration — (see Left/Right Brain Alignment)

Cellular level — Referring to a microscopic physical and mental level of information, based upon the assumption that every cell has all of the information of the whole body. MRT is used to access information from this level at any age of our lives from the day we were born, even in the womb.

Chakras — Energy centers located along the spinal column, above the head and below the feet. The five above the head connect to the five below the feet, making a capsule of energy around our bodies, which is adversely affected by electromagnetic radiation and emotional stress. Chakras connect to the acupuncture meridians that flow through our bodies, feeding energy to organs and muscles.

Chiropractic — "A theraputic system based upon the premise that disease is caused by interference with nerve function, the method being to restore normal condition by adjusting the segments of the spinal column." (W.E.D.)

Choice — Choice happens when there is "no need." When you say you needed to do something, just remember that you have given away your choice to choose; so in a fashion, you have chosen to be a victim of your mind.

Collusion — A secret (subconscious) understanding between two people prejudicial to another. Thus you listen not for the objective truth, but for your own reasons to agree with someone else about their opinions of a third person. You can empathize with their experience, while not advocating this as the only vantage point for truth.

Context — What influences the meaning or affects the set of circumstances that surround a particular event, situation, etc. The content is the situations and circumstances of your life and the context is how you hold (interpret & experience) the content.

Compensation — When a decision has been made, such as "I am *not loved*," the mind must compensate for that belief by doing all it can to *be loved* and prove it false.

Complaining — A way of blaming that *appears* to be positive, which always has a negative effect. Complaining is **not** a way to get what you want. Instead, it is a way to avoid expressing *feelings* and *want*s, which requires commitment and responsibility.

Compassion — A deep feeling of caring that understands clearly through experiencing a person's thoughts and feelings and with an ability to walk in their shoes. The ability to empathize supports people to take responsibility for their life and heal their problem, while sympathy may keep one feeling like a victim.

Consciousness — Heightened awareness. Able to share one's thoughts and feelings in difficult situations. Spiritually aligned and aware of the consequences of one's actions.

Deception — An unconscious lie that you tell yourself or another. See Self-Deception.

Declaration — See affirmation.

Deep-rooted fear — A fear related to a phobia, such as fear of heights, fear of the dark, fear of death, etc.

Divine Purpose — Why you came to earth at this time in these circumstances to express a particular aspect of God.

Dominion — The power to rule and be in authority over one's subtle energy fields, as well as in all areas of one's life. To dominate natural substance (of the earth) and reign over one's own body and life.

Double Mindedness — A condition where your left brain thoughts and your right brain feelings/intuition are not aligned. Therefore, you emotionally experience going in two directions at once, which gets in the way of accomplishing your goal.

Dyslexia — This is the result of having a gap between the left & right brain function in relation to learning. This can cause slow reading, transposing letters or numbers, less comprehension and frustration. See Emotional Dyslexia.

Ego Defenses — Ploys for the mind to survive in an intimidating world. We all acquire a set of *habitual* and *unconscious defensive devices*. These survival mechanisms bolster our sense of self acceptance and "self-rightness" when handling anxiety, guilt, or emotionally threatening situations. Ego Defenses alleviate post traumatic stress; soften failure or disappointment; reduce frustration and emotional conflict and protect us against acting out dangerous impulses. Though still part of immature behavioral patterns, they can assist you to watch your mind in action.

In our early development stages these coping and adjusting behaviors are predictable and to some extent even healthy. As we mature, we are invited to shed defensive escape mechanisms and face difficulties directly. Maturation is about attaining a rich, meaningful life, not avoiding discomfort or hiding from feelings. It is about being open to know the truth no matter how uncomfortable that might be.

Electromagnetic radiation — Radiation consisting of electromagnetic waves (electric and magnetic waves) including radio waves, light, x-ray, and gamma rays. I am usually referring to the energy emitted from man-made electrical devices that affect the energy field of your body in an adverse way; such as microwaves, fluorescent lights, T.V.s, computers, etc.. The over saturation of these rays causes a short circuiting of the body's electrical currents and a shrinking of the body's electrical field, which can affect your energy level and your immune system.

Emotional Dyslexia — A condition of dyslexia that comes and goes according to the emotional environment; such as when one is with a certain person or in a specific situation. An automatic "switching off" happens, causing the left and right hemisphere of the brain to disconnect and only be able to function one side at a time; the result being that the person becomes super emotional or super logical and does not integrate thoughts and feelings holistically. This emotional-based response usually relates to an earlier negative emotional experience.

Emotion Points — Testing areas on the body that disclose hidden emotions on a cellular or subconscious level. See Trigger Point Testing.

Full Potential — The MOST and BEST that is possible for one to be.

Grace — Unmerited favor. A way of receiving a free gift or favor without deserving it, with the understanding that there are no strings attached.

Holy Spirit — The third expression of the Infinite Godhood, the Spirit of God, the Everywhere Presence, witnessing and testifying to all truth. The disciples of Christ were baptized in the Holy Spirit on the day of Pentecost before they went out to teach and preach with power. Holy Spirit baptism is the gift that Christ is bestowing today upon all those who seek it for the building of the kingdom. See Baptism of Fire.

Homeopathy — The method of treating disease by using minute doses (such as 1,000,000 to 1) of a toxic substance to create in a well person the same symptoms to those of the disease. A dilution and shaking process leaves only the electrical field of the toxin, whereby the body's own immune system becomes alarmed to fight the problem.

Immature Ego State — The cluster of emotions based upon unresolved feelings that were judged, suppressed, and had a perpetration attached. The Immature Ego State is what reappears when in a similar upset when older, showing that one's reaction stayed the same as when young (immature). Immature ego states can be observed when you see a grown person behaving as a little child.

Inner Guidance — The direction that you inherently "see" and "hear" with your heart and soul. May be referred to as the High Self, Light of Christ, Light of Truth, Spirit of God, intuition, divine conscience. Also, see Holy Spirit.

Inside job — This refers to the possibility that the answer, as well as the problem, lies within you. It is not what happens to you that matters, it is **how** you handle it and what you choose to do with that information.

Irony — Expressing a meaning which is different from, and often the direct opposite of the literal meaning. A manner of organizing a work so as to give full expression to contradictory or complementary impulses, attitudes, etc. especially as a means of indicating detachment from a subject, theme, or emotion.

Judging — The mind drawing a conclusion before all of the evidence is in. The conclusion the mind draws is to make itself feel *comfortable* through proving it is right, proper, or justified.

Kalos Health Facilitator — A person who is certified in applying The Kalos Process and the Ten Priority System to support people to participate in their healing process to heal the cause of their problem in the fastest way possible. See: *"What Is A Health Facilitator?"* at the end of this book.

Kalos Methodology — A set or system of methods, principles, and rules for understanding symptoms and causes in any area of one's life. A healing discipline and full potential development art to achieve success physically, mentally, emotionally and spiritually.

Kalos Process, The — A spiritual process to understand and alleviate inner turmoil and emotionally based decisions that have affected one's life in a way that interferes with achieving success physically, mentally and emotionally. The Kalos Process is a process to: "See the truth to be set free of perpetrations and emotional blocks hindering one's healing process."

Left Brain — Relating to one's *thoughts*, as opposed to one's *feelings*. Referring to the left hemisphere of the brain that relates to functioning through practicality and logic. Left brain dominance relates to processing information in a lineal manner, one step at a time, to arrive at conclusions.

Left and Right Brain Alignment — This is the process of bringing agreement and electrical connection to the right and left hemispheres of the brain. This connection makes it possible for the brain to function more clearly using both the *right brain feelings* and intuition, as well as the *left brain thoughts* and logic. Aligning both thoughts and feelings supports you to accomplish any goal much easier. See Dyslexia and Emotional Dyslexia.

Maturing up — This process changes the way you look at a life situation from the viewpoint of a child to the viewpoint of an adult. You mature the old lie, fear, perpetration to its Full Potential (another part of yourself). This assists you in gathering information and answering questions pertaining to the objective of your Kalos Process.

Medical Cause — is the physiologically detectable sequences in the pathology of a disease. Kalos usually goes to the underlying cause behind the medical cause. See also Cause.

Mental Programming — The automatic workings of one's mind based upon survival programming. A storehouse of information on every experience that one has ever encountered. Since each experience builds upon another, mental programming builds to create patterns of automatic behavior to keep one in their comfort zone.

Muscle Response Testing (MRT) — The practical use of the science of Applied Kinesiology through performing a muscle response test by isolating a specific muscle to access information at a cellular level. As a direct connection to the brain through the muscle, MRT is used throughout this text to obtain information and reprogram the subconscious mind.

Natural Laws — "A principle or body of laws considered as derived from nature, right reason, or religion and as ethically binding in human society." (W.E.D.)

Naturopathy — The method of treating disease through the use of foods, herbs, supplements, exercise, heat and other natural resources, including vibrational medicine and correcting one's mental attitude. The assumption is that nature always has the cure near the problem. The basic premise is to apply natural non-toxic supports to assist the body's innate healing ability.

Neuro-vascular Holding Points — Located mainly on the head. They require a light touch to strengthen a weak muscle, improve circulation between muscles and organs and support the releasing of trapped emotions from a subconscious level.

Open Eyed Process — The first part of The Kalos Process to resolve problems on a conscious level, where the cause of that problem does not begin before memory.

Osteopathy — A therapeutic system of healing based upon soft tissue manipulation of the muscles and of manipulating the spine to restore or preserve health. Nutritional support is also recommended. In some states Osteopaths prescribe drugs, as do medical doctors.

Paradox — A statement or proposition seemingly self-contradictory or absurd, yet in reality expressing a possible truth. Both sides of possible truth.

Perpetration — Something you believe to be true that isn't. A subconscious self-deception or hidden agenda that you try to compensate for by proving it is not true, which then creates living out of the compensation for it. Often referred to as a lie that you believe about yourself, such as "I am not loved" or "I am not good enough." Core programming based upon a decision with a deception attached.

Positive intent — A want or desire that stems from an honorable source, such as: "Behind every feeling and action is a positive intent."

Precept — "A commandment or direction given as a rule of action or conduct; a maxim. A rule or law; a written order issued pursuant to law. Direction, order, prescription, guide or instruction." (W.E.D.)

Prime Attitude Game — A pattern of programming that is constantly running your mind and affecting your attitude in all of the aspects of your life; such as, "I'm not understood" or "I never get my share" or "There is never enough." Notice all "attitude games" contain limitations.

Proclaim — To speak in a way that acknowledges your word is powerful. "To announce or declare in an official or formal manner." (W.E.D.)

Reaction — What happens when the subconscious is triggered into automatic behavior in the unhealed (immature) aspects of one's life, rather than a conscious response. Mentally or emotionally going back to an earlier, less mature time. "A reverse movement or tendency; an action in a reverse direction or manner." (W.E.D.)

Reality — The way "it is" looking from the eyes of spirit. This term may be in contradiction to what one's mind thinks is real. Something that can be "seen" on a physical level or experienced on a nonphysical level. A real thing or fact.

Renewing your mind — To change the bottom line programming of your mind from fear-based to trust and love-based, restoring a **spiritual** context to its functioning. A continual knowing that everything is working a benefit and will be fine no matter what the situation appears to be, as opposed to one's fundamental survival-based programming, which subconsciously runs one's behavior. Sometimes referred to as transformation. You transform your life through the *renewing of your mind*. This is not to mean "positive thinking," but to mean a perpetual positive attitude.

Responsibility — The ability to respond or owning your ability to make your own choices. "The state or fact of being answerable or accountable, as for something within one's power, control, or management." (W. E.D.)

Restitution — To restore losses or compensate for damages one has incurred against another. To make amends and restore a loving relationship with emotional support as well.

Right Brain — Referring to the right hemisphere of the brain, which relates to pictures, creativity, art, intuition and feelings; not logic.

See the truth — A discovery. To awaken to reality and simply see "what is," as opposed to an opinion of what is so through one's belief system.

Self-Deception — A belief that causes a contradiction in the way you act versus what you say. See Perpetration.

Single mindedness — A state of being aligned in both left and right hemispheres of the brain - in both *thoughts* and *feelings*.

Soul — A combination of: The will, mind and emotions, separate from the physical body. Often referred to as a quality of evolutionary expansion and growth. The soul evolves, yet functions in conjunction with spirit.

Special Place — This is your "Kingdom Within," a special place where only you can go. This is a place within you, where you invite your special Advisors (a part of yourself), ask questions, receive answers and gain valuable support.

Spiritual Principles — Laws that go beyond physical understanding, yet affect our physical world and our aliveness; such as the law of giving, which creates abundance; the law of forgiveness, which creates healing; and the law of faith, which causes miracles to happen.

Surrogate testing — A way of testing small children, invalids, yourself, and even animals. It is the process of using one person's muscle to test another person. Surrogate testing demonstrates how the electrical currents of one body are transmitted to another body through touch, just as how many people can join hands and touch an electrical fence, yet only the one on the end gets the shock.

Transformation — The act of moving or changing from one form to another, as a tree is transformed into lumber. A transformed state is still made of the same "stuff." It simply takes on a different purpose and meaning. Transforming one's life is to alter one's purpose from self-centeredness to consciousness beyond the self, incorporating the whole of humanity. To live for the benefit of others, unconditionally caring and humbly loving all creatures, even with risking one's comfort, is to transform one's life.

Transmutation — The act of changing into a completely different nature or substance, form or condition. Using the above example of the tree, would be to burn the lumber in a fire, turning it into heat, light and ashes. A conversion process takes place, such as pride turns into humility and greed changes into contribution without seeking personal gain from the giving. It is a type of transformation. Even hate can turn into love when transmuted by "truth," such as in a Kalos Process.

Trigger Points — Specific places on the body you touch and use MRT to determine internal conditions and subconscious information programmed within the memory banks of the cells. This includes Emotional Point Testing.

Truth — I refer to "the truth" as being "what is so." This can mean as an individual or to the whole. Truth many times takes on the energy of what the group agrees "is so." I am **not** using "truth" as a doctrine or belief, but rather as a discovery or an experience of reality (spirit), which does not need explanation or defending, only observing. You can "Know the truth and the truth can set you free!"

Unconditional Love — Supernatural loving with no conditions attached to that loving. Relates to loving ALL in the same manner with no respecter of persons, as opposed to the mind's way of loving conditionally before it is renewed. Also referred to as Godly love or agape (in Greek).

Unclean Spirits — The biblical term for thought forms that can attach to a person's energy field, referred to as: *"Oppressive spirits"* and *"Possessive spirits."* Some refer to them as energy forms. They are different from disembodied spirits, whom have lived here and died.

Universal Principle — A specific viewpoint to look at life for identifying perpetrations and resolving reactionary behavior that comes from a judgmental state.

Vibrational medicine — Based upon the premise that all matter is energy. A form of medicine that applies Einstein's paradigm, seeing human beings as networks of complex energy fields that interface with physical/cellular systems. Uses specialized forms of energy to positively affect those energetic systems to bring them to balance.

Well-being — Energetic, a state of being well and healthy - physically, mentally, emotionally and spiritually, having a zest for life!

Word of authority — Declaring or proclaiming a statement that causes the changing of events or energy. Speaking from the Spirit or under the influence of the Holy Spirit. When using the Universal Principles to observe life's events there is an experience of seeing with the eyes of authority. Using the Word of Authority is a way of taking charge of your life and moving energy immediately in its simplest form.

Index

A

B

C

D

E

H

I

J

K

L

V

W

A Note of Appreciation

Dear Reader:

You are acknowledged and appreciated for taking this guide book's specific steps in transformational healing and in manifesting your full potential.

We encourage you to practice the techniques and processes. You are invited to continue exploring the laws, axioms, precepts and principles.

May you associate with others who will support your wellness in joy and gratitude. Come join us in a Kalos Seminar.

Thank You

KALOS™ PUBLISHING
Envisioning a Transformed World

QUICK ORDER FORM
1-800-77-KALOS

Credit Card: Phone: (800) 775-2567 Fax: (800) 335-2567
Postal: P.O. Box 270817, San Diego, CA 92198-2817
Payment must be included with order.

Please Print

Phone _____

Name _____

Address _____

City _____ State _____ Post Code _____

QTY	TITLES		AMOUNT
	Heal the Cause!	one copy – $19.50 ea. 2 or more – $17.50 ea.	
	A New Day in Healing	one copy – $12.00 ea. 2 or more – $10.00 ea.	
	Pamphlet: How to Protect Yourself from Electromagnetic Radiation	1 to 4 – $2.00 ea. 5 or more – $1.50 ea.	
		Subtotal	
		Canadian Orders add 30%	
		CA Residents add 7.5% Sales Tax	
	USA BOOK SHIPPING: $3.50/first book + $1 ea additional book USA PAMPHLET: $0.75/first copy + .35 ea. additional copy *OVERSEAS ORDERS WILL BE BILLED FOR 1st CLASS*		
		TOTAL ORDER	

Payment ☐ Check ☐ Visa ☐ Master Card

Card Number _____

Name on Card _____

Expiration Date ____ / ____ / ____ _____

Signature

I understand that I may return book(s) in saleable condition within 30 days for a full refund for any reason, no questions asked.